aftershock

For Esther and Bethany

aftershock

ADRIAN HOLLOWAY

survivor

First published 2004

ISBN 1 84291 176 7

2 3 4 5 6 7 8 /08 07 06 05 040

Survivor is an imprint of
KINGSWAY COMMUNICATIONS LTD
Lottbridge Drove, Eastbourne BN23 6NT, England.
Email: books@kingsway.co.uk

Book design and production for the publishers by
Bookprint Creative Services, P.O. Box 827, BN21 3YJ, England.
Printed in U.S.A.

thanks

I am indebted to my wife Julia in more ways than anyone reading this book could imagine. *Aftershock* was written while we were moving as a family from Oasis Church, Birmingham, to help start ChristChurch, central London, and without Julia's constant help this book could never have been started, let alone finished.

I'd also like to thank David Stroud, Adrian Hurst and everyone at Oasis Church, Birmingham, who released me from my usual responsibilities for an intense period of book writing. Oasis has been a fantastic experience for us. We love you all!

Where I have unknowingly repeated the words of other authors or speakers, I apologise.

introduction

Hi! My name's Daniel. I'm a freak. I'm a weirdo. Why? Well, for starters, I used to be dead. I was your average British teenager until I was in a car crash and died.

So the very fact that I'm here telling you I used to be dead means that I've kissed goodbye to normality. For example, when I'm at a party, people dare their friends to go up and talk to the 'near-death-experience-kid'. But that only makes me unusual.

What makes me weird is that I met someone while I was dead who's still with me now. He's right here beside me now. In fact he's inside me now, and I'm thrilled with him. Catching my weirdness yet?

Let me change tack and try to connect with you logically. You know that there are people who claim to have died and then come back. There's a certain type of magazine that'll print their stories. When you're in the waiting room at the dentist, you look at that pile of reading matter. You discard the stuff about making your home look beautiful and dressing your children the same colour as the curtains. Then you see a headline about 'Jane's Journey' – how so and so died on the operating table, rose up out of their body and looked down on everyone in the theatre. Then they saw a white light, lots of flowers and their grandma, but then they're down from the ceiling and back in their body. It's all so beautiful.

If I were being paid by the University of California, I could trawl through every dentist's waiting room in the world, compile all such accounts, analyse the data, identify common features, interpret them in ways that make you feel better, and then write a stinking blockbuster. They're called NDEs – that's Near Death Experiences.

But I claim to have had a fully dead experience. Physically, chemically, I was fully dead, as my hospital records show. And unlike the NDEs you might have read about, most of which were good trips, mine was bad. So bad that I'd back my chances of getting on any daytime chat show. At the very least, I would expect to make *Trisha*

But having a bad trip is one thing. What's freakish with me is that when I came round, I was in love with a Jewish carpenter called Jesus of Nazareth. I knew off by heart bits of the Bible I'd never read. In fact I'd never even opened a Bible, let alone read any of it. There was nothing in my background to suggest any sort of religious interest. I had no previous knowledge of Christianity. It wasn't in there waiting to come out. I got it all beyond the grave! I found out that Christianity is true! My mum sent me to the psychiatrist – which I don't blame her for, but let's not go there yet.

The accident itself was caused by brake failure on a lorry that was right behind us on the morning drive to school. I was sitting in the back of my mum's car with my sister Kate next to me. Mum was driving with a pot plant on the passenger seat next to her. Then suddenly, this lorry thumped into us from behind, right into my seat. I was knocked out immediately, and they reckon I died about 20 minutes later.

And then I got the shock of my life! Some of you may have read about it, but now I'd like to tell you the rest of the story . . .

chapter 1

It must have looked like a scene from a soap opera: my mum and sister crouched round the bed watching the tragic teenager lying motionless. I was dead. Kate told me later that Mum persuaded the hospital to bend the rules and allow my immediate family in for two minutes to 'pay their last respects to the body'. So when I opened my eyes, I nearly gave them a heart attack!

I don't remember opening my eyes, but I do remember hearing a shriek, and then my mum's hysterical crying. It was the first sign of life I'd shown. Then lots of shouting as a medical team crashed through double doors, wired me up and plugged me in. If you've never breathed through a facemask, I can only imagine it's similar to being an astronaut. Every breath sounds like you're making history. And I was.

Back from the dead, all I could think about was Jesus! He was mine and I was his! I had to tell everyone what happens when you die. That you get judged, and that you need forgiveness before you get judged. That you need Jesus' forgiveness in this life. That when you die it's too late. I wanted to tell my mum, who I loved so much. I wanted to tell Kate. I was so relieved that they were still alive!

Kate and my mum were both wearing dressing gowns. I

guess they were being kept in for observation, having been injured in the same accident as me, but they looked absolutely fine, apart from a cut on my sister's chin.

Try as I might, I couldn't say anything. I couldn't even feel my legs. Was I paralysed? I could hear things, but I couldn't speak. My jaw was locked and my tongue felt all leathery and too big for my mouth.

I fell asleep. My first few minutes of being a Christian had been a massive frustration – so much to say, and yet no ability to say it. But I was alive and ready to rumble! First, though, I wanted to know about the accident.

When you can't talk, people obviously assume that you're deaf as well, because on one occasion I heard Mum asking a doctor, 'How much should we tell him?' The doctor replied: 'It's up to you.'

The next day she asked, 'Should we tell him about the others?' This really got me wondering. What others? Mum and Kate were the only people in the car with me and they looked as if they'd escaped with nothing more than cuts and bruises. Who were 'the others'? Other people who got hurt in the accident? But we were a crummy little car hit by a lorry. That's like an eggshell versus a tank, isn't it? So there can't have been any 'others'.

At this stage it felt like I was only awake for a couple of hours a day, but the next clue was when I overheard Kate mention the word 'funeral'.

Then I woke up one afternoon to find a couple of complete strangers standing at the end of my bed dressed in black. I'd had lots of medical faces in my room, but the only proper visitors were relatives. I hadn't even been allowed friends. And now here were a random smartly dressed couple looking like death warmed up. He was balding with glasses, dressed all in black apart from his white shirt, and she was big with a black veil on her hat. This was spooky.

They smiled when they realised I could see them. 'It really is very kind of you to let us come,' the middle-aged man said to Mum.

'That's quite all right, Mr Mason,' she replied. 'We want to do anything we can to help.'

What was going on? How come all of a sudden this 'Mr Mason' and his wife had got promoted over Mikey, Pete, Andy and all my other mates I was desperate to see? Mum needed to sort her priorities on the hospital visitors front.

'The school have been so brilliant about it. In fact, everyone's been brilliant,' Mum continued. And then came the moment I'll never forget: 'Did Daniel know Becky at all?' Mum asked.

It didn't hit me at first because I knew at least three Beckys. Then it was bombshell time when I put first and second names together . . . Becky Mason! Was Becky Mason dead? Becky Mason was the only Christian I'd ever known. The one person who could have told me about Jesus before I died! Was this her parents on their way to her funeral? And had Mum let them in because, somehow, Becky Mason had died in the same accident as me? That's the only sense I could make of it.

I'd used Becky's name as a swear-word when I was dead and facing for ever without forgiveness. I remember that I had wanted to give Becky Mason a piece of my mind. 'Oi Becky,' I'd wanted to shout. 'Why didn't you tell me? Only a matter of life and death, Becky! Or wasn't it important enough?' I'd felt cheated that I was dead and facing judgement and it was all too late. Any old day of the week, Becky Mason could have stopped me in the corridor at school, pinned me against the lockers, and said, 'Look, Dan, it's like this . . . when you die, you get judged and everything you've ever done gets laid out before you. It's all recorded in books, and you're gonna realise you're not perfect. You're not perfect enough for a perfect heaven. None of us are! That means you're facing eternal separation from God. Eternal death, Dan. You know – hell and all that. But God loves us so much that he sent Jesus to die in our place. Jesus is real. You need to accept his death in your place now! If you do you'll go to heaven. Listen to me while there's still time!'[1]

She could have explained why it's a problem for us to ignore God, and sin against him. She could have explained that we deserve punishment for our sin. She could have told me that Jesus died on the cross as a substitute, taking the punishment of all who trust in him. She could have drummed it into me that God so loved Daniel Adams that he gave his only Son Jesus to die in my place. She could have told me that forgiveness was available right now through faith in Jesus. She could have told me how great it was to enjoy a relationship with Jesus in this life.

But she didn't. She never said a word. I only found out she was a Christian on the grapevine. It was just something that was a bit odd about her. You know how everyone's got something different about them? One girl's got a big nose, another has a boyfriend who's 34, another's rumoured to still be a virgin. I suppose, one day, someone had said, 'Did you know that Becky Mason is one of those born-again Christians?' It had registered, by which I mean I think I remember being surprised to hear she was 'one of them'. I thought she was OK. Not the religious sort perhaps, but I hadn't really given it a moment's thought.

All things being equal, though, if Becky *had* slammed me against the lockers and off-loaded the truth about life, the universe and everything, I wouldn't have listened. I would have thought she was a nutter, and wondered whether I'd fancy her if she changed her hair and lost some weight.

Even if she'd taken the subtle approach, and drip by drip told me about how much God loved me, by sidling up to me in the lunch queue and then bumping into me 'accidentally on purpose' here, there and everywhere around the school, I probably would have told her, 'Look, Becky, I appreciate you taking the trouble and all, but it's . . . well, it's great for you, but it's not for me. I'm not really interested. I'm not religious.'

Becky was dead! I felt dreadful. But then, like a shot of adrenaline into my bloodstream, I thought, 'Hang on a minute! If Becky's dead, then she's with Jesus now!' Immediately I wanted to go back. Just the thought of being with Jesus sent my head spinning. I thought of Becky – this fairly nondescript girl I'd never really paid any attention to. And to think that right now she's with Jesus.

But I still didn't know that she was definitely dead. Of course, I couldn't ask because I couldn't talk. But the following day we had a breakthrough.

'Daniel, if you can hear me, blink once for "yes".' The more attractive of the two nurses showed some initiative. At last, communication I could respond to, because I could blink!

Over the next week I did a lot of blinking, and then one morning it was as if someone had flicked a recovery switch on in my body. They brought me some toast, and without realising it I said 'thanks' out loud! Later the same day, I felt my legs go all tingly. I hadn't even bothered to get worried about what it would be like to be paralysed. Only now did the thought of being disabled send a shudder through me.

'Can you feel your legs?' the doctor asked. My 'yeah!' sent Mum into a lap of honour round the room. I love my mum!

'Dear God,' I prayed silently, 'please may Mum find out what you're really like. That you're not religious or boring or non-existent. That you're real and exciting and knowable. That you're a person, for crying out loud!'

Gradually I got my speech back, and my upper body movement. I wondered why God didn't just give me everything back straight away. But anyway, slowly I was getting back to normal.

Of course, I pitched straight in and told Mum and Kate everything that had happened while I was dead. I had to do it in bits and pieces 'cos I got so excited about it, and tired myself out describing the sequence of events. I wanted to do everything justice: judgement, Jesus on the throne, the books, the entrance to hell. I was gushing descriptions of each moment. It was all crystal clear to me.

Are you expecting me to tell you they were instantly converted? Well, they weren't. They just sat there looking completely blank. No questions. Just concern. It was a response I was going to have to get used to. 'He's got religion,' my mum said to the less attractive nurse, still thinking I couldn't hear. 'How does he suddenly know all this stuff?'

After thousands of years of speculation and enquiry about whether there's a God and what happens when you die, it's a bit demoralising to discover the answer and then have your own mum not believe you. I thought to myself, 'It's early days. Perhaps she thinks I'm brain damaged.' At the very least, seeing as I could now talk, I could finally ask her about our visitors, the Masons.

Mum told me that the mystery couple were linked to the accident. Remember when we had been shunted from behind by the lorry and had gone up and over the kerb? Well, with it being 8.30 am in the morning on a school day, there was a better than average chance that some poor kid was going to get hit by a car flying across the pavement at 40 mph. It could have been any one of the 1,000 students who walk next to that road near the school entrance every day. It just happened to be Becky Mason, the one Christian I'd ever known. She smacked her head on the concrete pavement.

So Becky was dead. How on earth were her parents coping? Were they Christians? I carried on with the questions. Mum had resigned herself to telling me the whole gruesome story of the accident, and in fact she was relieved to get all the details off her chest. I was probably supposed to be traumatised by re-living it all, but I wasn't particularly. It seemed quite detached from me. Like a separate event.

As we talked on, I felt Mum wanted me to ask about the lorry driver. But why? I'd expected her to be angry with the lorry driver. I'd expected her to be threatening court action against him. She was the type.

'So who was driving the lorry?'

'You really want to know?' Mum replied looking worryingly close to enthusiastic.

When I nodded, she said something that almost left me speechless: 'OK, you can meet him tomorrow. His name's Alan. I'll bring him in to see you.'

I simply couldn't believe it. Mum was apparently on speaking terms with a man who'd nearly robbed her of her only son and caused Becky's death. Why was she being so positive about someone I'd expected her to hate? She'd even lined him up for a visit!

The next day, visiting time couldn't come round quickly enough. I was going to meet someone who'd killed me, even if it was accidentally. Would he be upset to see me in hospital? Was he going to cry? What does a crying lorry driver look like anyway?

Then Mum came in, and gave me a sort of pep talk about meeting him. Lorry driver man was obviously just round the corner. I could see him in silhouette through the curtains, moving his weight from one foot to the other. It felt all spooky again, like when Becky's parents had come in.

Then Mum said, 'Er . . . Dan, I'm afraid I haven't been entirely straight with you. I know you're wondering why Alan and I are friends, and we'll get to that, but in the meantime I need to tell you that Alan's here because he's got some bad news for you.'

'What bad news?' I snapped back, still wondering why my mum was on first name terms with this guy.

And then in he came, wearing a huge white neck brace. Whiplash would make sense, wouldn't it? Facially, he was one of those people who you can tell was probably considered good-looking in his day. Now he was sagging everywhere, like a flat tyre you can still just about drive on. His stomach was hanging over his belt. He'd made no attempt to co-ordinate his blue T-shirt with his brown leather jacket and golden chain with a cross on it. He looked like London taxi drivers do on telly. He was one of those people who turn out to be like a caricature of what you think they're going to look like. A real-life cartoon version of himself. I expected his interests to be stocks, shares and greyhounds.

'All right, son?' he asked in a rather too familiar way. He obviously didn't know quite how to pitch it. Having tried the upbeat approach, he then corrected himself. 'I'm so sorry about what happened.'

I launched straight in to what was becoming my standard response: 'Don't be sorry, because . . . er . . . look, I know this is going to sound strange, but while I was dead I got a taste of what happens when you die, and, well, er . . . Alan . . . I met Jesus!'

'I know.'

'You do?' I said, incredulously.

'Yes, I know because your mother told me all about it. I know you met Jesus, and oh, Emma would have been so pleased to hear you say that.'

'Who's Emma?' He'd mentioned her in the past tense.

'Dan, I'm afraid someone else died in the crash that I caused.'

'Becky,' I said, feeling relieved that it was only the Becky Mason story again. 'I know about Becky.'

'No, there was someone else as well as Becky. My daughter

Emma was in the lorry cabin next to me. She's dead, Daniel. She nearly went through the windscreen.'

I was too shocked to say anything. I simply looked at Mr Cartoon Lorry Driver and went blank. Time stood still. I think I just looked around the room shaking my head.

'But Dan,' he went on. 'Emma was a Christian! I'm here to tell you that Emma was the brightest, most vibrant young Christian you could possibly imagine, and nothing could have pleased her more than being called home to meet her Saviour.'

I gasped, then looked at Mum to see if she was as gob-smacked as I was by what he'd said. Was it really possible for people to be that positive about their own children being dead? Clearly it was! No wonder Alan the lorry driver had made such an impression on my mum. I'd never met anyone like him. I would have expected any parent so unfazed by death to be a bit unhinged and wild-eyed. Yet Alan, who'd so neatly fitted my category of a stereotypical lorry driver, was equally authentic when talking about his daughter being in heaven. I felt responsible for the whole calamity, even though I knew I wasn't. Yet here was the man who, I suppose, was responsible for the accident, and it had cost him his own daughter, and he was coping!

'Daniel,' Mum said, 'Alan and I have been talking about what you told me about . . . er . . . Jesus,' she mumbled his name into her shoes, clearly embarrassed, 'and I think Alan can help you.' It sounded patronising, but it wasn't. Clearly my mum was a changed woman. Previously, she'd never been able to get over things. She'd always be harking back to stuff that had happened to her years ago. What happened with Dad was the worst of it: a divorce with no closure, an open wound. She wasn't very good at moving on.

Yet here she was being all mature. Why? Just a month ago she'd gone through the most traumatic thing that had ever happened to her – a car accident that almost destroyed her and her two children – and here she was coming on all sensible about it. She seemed to be taking the view that we were lucky to be here and that it didn't matter whose fault the accident was. It was obvious to everyone in the room that we had something to learn from Alan.

The next day, Alan was back. 'Look, Dan, your mum wants me to talk to you about the God thing. She doesn't understand, but I do, and she realises that. But she also wants you to see a psychiatrist.'

'What?'

'Hang on . . . And then she's happy for you to see your friends. She's not wanted them to come until now. That's the deal. She knows that you want to see your mates, but she's worried they might think you've lost it – you know, lost your marbles – if you tell them about judgement day and all.'

'Oh please!' I said, anger rising for the first time.

'But look at it from her point of view, Dan. She's got your best interests at heart. She doesn't want your friends to think you've gone mad.' And then, moving right up next to me, Alan whispered, 'Dan, I think I've gained your mum's confidence, which is pretty amazing considering it was my brakes that failed and me that caused the accident. You've got an awesome story to tell, and God's in this. I don't know why Emma died, I don't know why Becky died, I don't know why you experienced what you did and then came back, but I can see how God can bring some good out of all this mess. Just go along with your mum's scheme and I think I can see a way through for all of us.'

I had been desperately looking forward to seeing my friends. I knew that they would have wanted to see me, but Mum had been very evasive about who was allowed to visit and when. I was pleased I was going to get the chance I'd been waiting for. If anyone on this earth was going to be impacted by the change in me it was my closest friends Mikey,

Andy and Pete. If I saw this psychiatrist, Mum would then let me talk to my posse and that would be the start, I hoped, of the rest of my life. Surely this was why I'd been allowed back to earth: to tell the Petes of this world that there's a real God who loves them. I was a sort of matchmaker. I was going to play cupid between my mates and their Maker.

The psychiatrist thing had already been arranged. Alan's little chat was part of Mum's plan to make some sense out of the God talk I'd dumped on her and Kate. As it turned out, the visit of the shrink was a huge anti-climax. There was no 'Tell me about your childhood'. She didn't wear a white coat or have those bi-focal glasses, which I'd assumed were standard issue. She didn't have a deep soothing voice and there wasn't even a leather couch. I felt cheated. Dr Alice Bennett was her name. In her mid-40s, I'd imagine. 'So Dan, tell me what happened,' she said rather matter-of-factly.

I went through it slowly, as she made occasional notes, and smiled constantly. I started with how incredible it seemed to me to find out that when you're dead, you're not! The wow of consciousness. I talked about the grandeur of the angel, the bits of the Bible he read to me that had lodged in my mind. The majesty of Jesus, the Judge, on his great white throne. People being judged and sent away. The tour of the horrors of hell. The agonies, which still sent a shiver through me.

But here was Dr Shrink, sitting in front of me, who one day would stand before Jesus on judgement day. Where was she going when that great day arrived? To heaven or hell? 'Can I ask you, doctor – what do you think will happen to you when you die?'

'Daniel, I don't think we can ever know in this life.'

'But that's the whole point,' I replied, astonished that someone so intelligent couldn't see the irony of what she'd just said. 'The only way we can ever know what happens beyond death is if someone comes back. And even if you

19

don't believe a word I've said about what happened to me, Jesus has come back from the dead. And that's a fact of history.'

'Is it?' she asked, giving nothing away apart from an obvious hint that she thought it was a matter of debate.

I immediately realised that telling others wasn't going to be easy. If I took Dr Clever-Cloggs at face value, she was genuinely unsure whether Jesus did rise from the dead. *I* knew he had, but how could I convince her? I wasn't going to worry about it for the time being, because my mates were coming the next day and they knew what I used to be like. I was convinced that they'd have no possible way of explaining away the change in me.

It was a long night of anticipation. Having gone through the preliminaries with Alan (the acceptable face of Christianity as far as my mum was concerned) and the shrink (the reasonable face of all things reasonable), there I was the following afternoon, waiting for my three best friends to arrive.

I pretended to be asleep. They sort of tip-toed in, thinking that I was a fragile handle-with-care version of the Dan they used to know. I heard them sit down. Still silence.

'Aaagh!' I suddenly went.

They nearly died, jumping out of their chairs. 'Not funny, Dan,' Mikey said. He'd dyed his hair blond, which was a terrible mistake.

'What do you think you look like?'

'Mate, you're not looking too clever yourself,' Mikey replied. 'Your mum's been really funny about letting us see you. How the hell are you?'

I resisted the temptation to comment on hell. 'Yeah, I'm fine. Look, guys, I've got something to tell you all and it's going to take at least half an hour.'

'Dan, are you OK?' Pete asked.

'Never been better,' I replied, although this was plainly

ridiculous as far as they were concerned, looking at me in my hospital bed.

'You're going to give us a speech?' Pete asked taking off his baseball cap and saluting me like a soldier. 'What's going on, mate?'

'Listen up,' I said. 'I don't know if you know anything about what happened. I really died in the accident. You can ask the doctors. But listen, there's something beyond death. I experienced it all. It's exactly what the Bible says happens beyond death.'

'What the . . .' Andy tailed off.

'Mikey, Andy, Pete,' I used their names to sort of sound more dramatic, 'we've been living in a fantasy land. The last three years, we've been going through life together, never giving a moment's thought to whether there's a God, whether we owe him for even putting us on this planet, for even making this planet. But he's real. God made us. We all meet him when we die. Well actually, we meet Jesus . . .' and I was off, rattling through what had happened to me.

About 25 minutes later I came in to land by saying, 'We've been playing around with what's seemed like fun, but it's garbage compared to the sort of power and energy I'm talking about. You can know Jesus, guys. It's the utter business. You can feel like this.' I pointed to my chest to try and indicate that I was feeling this constant elation inside me. But I think they were so shell-shocked by my rapid-fire delivery that I'd lost them by this stage. 'So what do you think?'

The longest pause.

'Dan, you need help, mate,' Mikey said.

'No, hang on. What if he's right?' Andy broke in. 'How does he suddenly know all this stuff – all this spirit-realm information?'

'You're not making this up are you, Dan?' Pete asked. 'Because if you are it's in pretty poor taste.'

'This is from the heart, guys. Look, I'm still me. I'm still Dan. I haven't gone mad. It's just that there's something out there that none of us has ever thought about. It's like this insane secret. God's real, but they don't tell you on TV or at parties or in clubs, or ever. As if it doesn't matter. But it does! He does. He's fantastic. It's like a high, but you don't come down.'

'I don't believe in God,' Mikey said.

'But why not?' I asked.

'I'm a scientist.' Of course, this was preposterous. He was a spotty teenager.

'So what?' I asked, getting a bit annoyed.

'Well, science has disproved the Bible,' Mikey said. 'We know so much more than they did thousands of years ago. Maybe they needed to believe in God back then.'

This was not going according to plan. Mikey, Pete and Andy were supposed to be thoroughly impacted by my compelling account of what's really beyond the grave. My first-hand knowledge was supposed to trump whatever ill-informed views we'd all previously held on the subject. They were meant to ask me all about what Jesus is really like, and want to know more. And then maybe we'd pray together. And then one by one my whole friendship circle would start to topple like dominoes, as King Jesus swept through.

'How can you prove God exists?' Mikey asked. 'How do you know God made us? What if we just happened? Why do we have to bring God into it? I mean, Dan, I'm not knocking what you're saying; it's just that you seem to have got faith and I haven't. I just go by what I can see and touch.'

'So how come Dan suddenly knows all this?' Andy asked, challenging Mikey.

'I dunno.'

'Exactly. It's a flipping miracle, that's what it is,' Andy said.

I liked the sound of this. Then a knock at the door. (I'd been moved into a different room by now.) It was Mum. She came in and it was reunions all round, and immediately we were off the subject.

I felt pretty knocked back by Mikey's scepticism. As they were leaving the room, I just had to go for it. 'Look, guys, you know I wouldn't lie to you. You know what we've gone through together. I'm telling you this because I want you to have this feeling. I want you to find out for yourselves how good Jesus is. You've got to listen to me. I don't want you to go to hell.' That word again. I'd embarrassed my mother.

The mood in the room frosted over, but I persisted: 'That's the reality. Life's not just some mysterious free gift that we just make the most of and then forget about. If we don't live for God, we face the consequences. Hell's awful. It's a nightmare, but it's a real nightmare.' I was losing them. 'Listen to me . . .' I was reaching out to them emotionally by this stage.

'Dan . . . look, you've changed so much,' Pete said. 'There are so many questions. Let's just chill and next time we can talk some more. It's great to have you back, mate. Respect and all that.'

'Bye, Dan,' Mikey said, but couldn't quite look at me as he said it. This wasn't good.

They left and I felt utterly crestfallen. My mum went out and I was left all alone.

'What's happening?' I said out loud to God. 'Why don't they believe me? What's going on?' I thought about Mikey's question: 'How do you know God made us? What if we just happened? Why do we have to bring God into it?' My answer was that I just knew. And if dying and meeting God myself wasn't good enough for Mikey, then I was stumped. I hadn't thought there'd be any need for answering questions. I'd thought people would just believe me. But the reality was that Mikey's question was the start of an earthquake. For the next year of my life I was going to ride the aftershock.

chapter 2

Out of hospital and back at home, I was a minor celebrity for a few weeks. Well, to be precise, I made the local paper.

It took me almost five months to recover enough to go back to school, initially in a wheelchair, then on crutches, before finally getting full movement back. I still got severe back pain and sharp twinges in my neck.

By the time I'd gone back to school, which was just after the Christmas holidays, I'd read loads of the Bible, so the novelty factor of 'How come Dan Adams knows so much about the Bible?' had worn off. Also, it was becoming obvious that I had missed so much work at school in my final year that I'd never catch up. It was January already. They decided that I could stay on and see out the year till the summer, but that I wouldn't have to do the exams. Then I could repeat all three terms with the year below starting in September. Well, that was a huge weight off my mind. I had from January till June at school with no pressure as far as work was concerned. I had a school to win for Jesus, so the more time the better.

Oh yeah – I need to tell you about church. I desperately wanted to meet Christians. These were the people who were sitting on the world's best-kept secret. Talk about a conspiracy of silence. My curiosity levels were sky high that first Sunday out of hospital.

Back at home with Mum and Kate, they'd already heard me ask a hundred times whether they could take me to church. I still needed a wheelchair at that stage so I was reliant on them to get anywhere. Mum agreed. Of course there was a local church we knew of: a huge building none of us had ever been in. I'd cycled past it throughout my childhood. But I'd never once thought, 'I wonder what it's like in there?' Church buildings had always been invisible to me.

So we bowled up ten minutes before the time advertised on the board for the service. Mum had got used to my 'experience' by now and she was becoming more sympathetic, though she didn't know what to make of it. I hoped the people at the church would back me up.

There were only about 50 people there. I don't know why I'd expected more, as I'd never seen any traffic round the church in all the years we'd lived on the same street. Then a blast on the organ and the teams processed in. There was a choir, who made up nearly half of the total congregation. They sang their way up the aisle, then snaked in two different directions either side of the altar. Then we all sat down and buried our faces in the books they'd dished out.

I have to say it was odd. But once I got into the words of the service I was on familiar ground. Every single thing they said was spot on. The words were a brilliant tribute to Jesus. They'd managed to sort of sum it all up concisely. The sentences worked in a sort of poetic way. But there was hardly anyone there to share in it.

Singing the hymns was a bit of a non-event. Amazing how embarrassed Mum was that she didn't know the tunes. Why should she? The offering bag came round and she dutifully put something in, making sure no one could see how much or how little it was. Others did the same. I thought this was all a bit false.

I tried to corner the vicar in the church hall afterwards. It was tea and biscuits. Not exactly my scene, but I had to start somewhere. These people seemed extremely sincere, but not very excited about Jesus. At least it wasn't obvious if they were.

I had two goes at talking to the priest. I didn't know what to call him. Eventually, on a second Sunday visit, we got talking, and he heard me out. He told me how interested he was in my experience and how pleased he was to hear of my rapid recovery after the accident. He was incredibly . . . nice.

But I wasn't satisfied. There had to be something on earth that came closer to the vibrancy and joy of heaven. Maybe Alan had the answer. Alan Meadowcroft, the lorry-driving villain of the piece, who'd become Mum's unlikely friend in the early weeks after the crash. I'd not seen him at all since leaving hospital. I found his number in Mum's mobile.

The next Sunday, Alan picked me up. He drove me to his church with his wife and their other two children. They all talked about Emma without any difficulty. I wondered whether they were for real. Were they in denial? 'But your daughter's just died!' I wanted to blurt out. 'Doesn't that churn you up? Shouldn't you be spitting nails or slitting your wrists about it?'

Evidently not, and when the service started I began to feel at home with them. Alan's amazing family were much like other people at this church. It was so different from the other one. The whole place was bobbing up and down within a few minutes. The prayers and songs were so heartfelt.

We chugged along, with the 'pastor' bouncing around the platform at the front in a slightly absurd way. And then I spotted a couple I'd honestly thought I'd never see again. There in the congregation were the Masons. I leaned over and asked Alan, 'What's the deal with the Masons?'

'Yes, they started coming here after the accident. They were at another church previously. God's doing a healing work there I think.'

Here were two families, recently bereaved, who both genuinely believed their daughters were now in a better place. A real place. With Jesus. I felt closer to Jesus among all these like-minded people. Funny that. I didn't think moral support would make any difference. In hospital I'd not felt the need for anyone else to join me on my mission. 'Fellowship' is what Christians call it. I was learning the lingo and feeling the benefit of having some people round me.

But I'm running ahead of myself. Let me tell you about Mikey. I wanted to do his question justice. It had been buzzing around in my head. But where could I start? How about at school? I was going to my English, history and media studies classes, but didn't have to do the written assignments unless I wanted to. No kidding! I'd been granted 'compassionate leave' on exams too, like I told you. Guess they thought I'd be happier kicking around with my mates at school than skulking around McDonald's all day on crutches, waiting for school to end so I could see everyone.

So what about Mikey's question about the origins of everything, and why does there have to be a God? I went to talk to Mr Foot, Head of Physics, during a break. I'd told him the day before that I wanted to ask him a bizarre question. I found him between lessons. For a physics teacher he looked surprisingly normal. Most of the others were socially challenged.

'How did the universe begin?' I asked him.

'Is this a joke, Dan, because I'm in a rush?' He hadn't taught me for three or four years, so he was a bit unsure of his ground.

'No kidding. How did the universe begin?'

'Well, the short answer is,' he put his file down, 'that most of us would think in terms of a Big Bang . . . um . . . the theory works something like this. At one time, all the matter in the universe that currently makes up our planets and galaxies

27

was condensed into a tiny speck smaller than a grain of sand. And then there was something called a quantum fluctuation – don't worry about quantum mechanics, no one really understands it – and then there was this almighty explosion of matter, and everything expanded, and here we are with a grown-up universe today. At least that's a tin-pot version of the current theory. No one's got this buttoned up. There are lots of loose ends at the moment. Lots of things we just don't know. But back in 1965, I think it was, they discovered out in space some radiation which looks like it was left behind by the Big Bang. It's the sort of signature of a Big Bang. So it looks like the universe had a beginning.'

'Isn't it obvious that the universe had a beginning?' I asked, thinking I'd believed that even before becoming a Christian.

'Well, yes, it is now. But for ages some people believed that the universe may have been eternal. In other words, that it had always existed. That it was just there. Then Einstein came along and everything changed.'

'Einstein?'

'Yes, Albert Einstein's General Theory of Relativity essentially pointed out that the universe is expanding. And if it's expanding and slowing down as it expands, which we now think it is, then it must have had a beginning. Look, I'm not really doing this justice.'

'OK. So why did the universe begin?'

'Why?' he said loudly, as if he had suddenly become hard of hearing.

'Yes, why? Why is there something rather than nothing?'

'Why? . . . I've absolutely no idea, Dan.'

'You don't know?' I asked incredulously.

'No, of course I don't. It's extremely unlikely that anything should exist. What do you think?'

What do I think? The Head of Physics was asking me for an opinion! This was what being a sixth-former was all about, I suppose. You know – interacting as an adult with people who treated you like scum just a few years previously because your collar wasn't done up.

'I think God made it.'

'Hah!' he grunted. 'Dan, I'm not religious myself, but good luck to you. If that's all, I've got a class waiting.' And with a swish, he was gone.

'Thanks, sir,' I said as he brushed past me. Well, fancy that! Mr Foot couldn't really account for why anything should exist. It's all extremely unlikely and perplexing as far as he is concerned. Yet bringing God into it was laughable. Why? What better explanation for an apparent miracle than God?

I needed more, though, 'cos I still didn't really know what I was on about. What would Alan say? He'd been a Christian for donkey's years. What would he say to a Mikey who just didn't believe in God?

Alan suggested I talk to a science teacher who went to his church. I wanted to call it 'our' church. And so after the evening meeting at our church, I sat down with Rob, who was only five years older than me, but was teaching at a rival school to ours. I explained Mikey's question, and what Mr Foot had told me.

'Yep, I'd go along with your Mr Foot,' he said.

'You would?' I said with a surprised 'what-no-religion-versus-science-pistols-at-dawn?' tone in my voice.

'Yes, in as much as he's being big enough to admit the limitations on scientific knowledge. Just because we have a model as to how the universe might have begun doesn't mean we know why it began. That's quite honest for a non-Christian scientist. You've actually done very well.' Rob was warming to his subject, and I was interested. 'Let's go back to square one. The first big question is, did the universe have a beginning?'

'That's a no-brainer. Yes!'

'But it's a hugely significant yes,' Rob replied. 'Just think if the answer was "no". Just think if the universe had always been there, like an eternal sock down the back of the radiator. If Mikey could argue that the universe has always been there, then he'd be able to say, "Dan, there's always been this thing called the universe. It's just there. Face it. It's timeless. It never had a beginning. No one made it. So there's no need for a creator. Game over."'

'OK, so why can't Mikey say that?'

'Because of what we've discovered. Ever heard of the Hubble telescope?'

'Er . . . no.'

'OK. It's named after this American astronomer called Edwin Hubble, and he discovered in 1929 that no matter where you look in the sky, nearly all the other galaxies are moving away from us. So the universe seems to be like an inflating balloon. Hubble's discoveries confirmed Albert Einstein's theory that the universe is expanding. It's getting bigger. All of a sudden, it looks like the universe had an explosive beginning and has been expanding ever since. This presented a problem for atheists who'd said that the universe never had a beginning.

'Besides, and this is another clue, if the universe had always existed, the stars and sun would have burned themselves out by now. Just like an apple decays if left long enough at the bottom of the fruit bowl, so any physical system becomes more random and less organised over time. We know the rotation of planets and moons is slowing down. If they'd always been there, they'd have run out of steam long before now. This is just a fact of life. It's called the Second Law of Thermodynamics.'[2]

'OK, let's see what Mikey says.' With that I was off, straight round to Mikey's house. No time like the present.

It was great to climb the stairs to Mikey's room, albeit on crutches. We'd had so many late night discussions there over the years. When I arrived, the guys just happened to be in session. Andy and Pete were spreadeagled across beanbags, and Mikey was holding court.

'Dan mate,' Pete began, 'great timing. Mikey's just been bringing us up to date with his latest conquest!'

'Oh yeah?'

'Guess who?'

'No idea.'

'Michelle Saunders!' Pete felt the need to stand and remind us of her impressive dimensions, as if any of us needed reminding.

'So what's happened to Anna, Mikey? I'm well out of touch.'

'Ho ho! That's what's so classic,' Pete carried on. 'He's still with Anna! And Mikey reckons we're all bound to secrecy.'

OK, so you need some background info. Anna is new at school, and she got together with Mikey while I was in hospital. But in the space of a few weeks, Mikey and Anna have become a major high-profile couple. She's good news. Genuine nice girl, who's slotted perfectly into our clique dynamic.

But Michelle Saunders is a goddess. The ultimate lower-school fantasy. She rules the school. Most of the girls hate her because she has everything. She's extraordinarily good-looking. I also like her sense of theatre. For example, she's made the daily grind of arriving each morning into an art form. We all just stumble in unnoticed and rain-soaked. But she screeches up to the school gates in her latest boyfriend's car, stereo blasting. Then it's a flick of the hair, and I've even found myself wondering what she would be wearing today. She spoke to me once when I was 14. I nearly died, and wrote two pages in my diary. She has a special smell that sort of stays in the corridor all day. Anyway, she's way out of Mikey's league and it was a sensation that she even knew who he was. How could it possibly have happened? When? Where?

We spent the next 20 minutes establishing that the whole thing wasn't a wind-up. Mikey insisted it was a one-night stand with Michelle and that Anna didn't need to know about it. But Andy, who apparently had set Mikey up with Anna in the first place, wasn't happy.

'Let's ask Dan what he thinks,' Andy said, obviously thinking that I might prove useful. 'Dan, shouldn't Mikey tell Anna the truth? Doesn't he owe it to her after all the time they've spent together?'

'How about it, Mikey?' I asked.

'Look, what Anna doesn't know won't hurt her. These things happen. I don't want to lose her. If there was something still going on between me and Michelle that would be different, but it's finished. It was just a spur of the moment thing. It was the right thing to do at the time. You don't pass up an opportunity like that. It needn't affect me and Anna. Why hurt her feelings?'

Pete weighed in: 'But what if Anna finds out?'

'She won't.'

'But what if she does?' Pete replied. 'Then you'll have to explain why you didn't come clean and tell her straight away. If you own up now, she might think, "Well, at least he's confessed." She might even stay with you.'

'I can't chance it,' Mikey said. 'You know it would be crazy to risk losing her unnecessarily.'

'But what if it was the other way round?' Andy said. 'What if she'd had a thing with some bloke and never told you? How would you feel?'

'She'd never,' Mikey answered.

'But what if she had? You'd want to know, wouldn't you?'

'Yeah,' Mikey said with a resigned sigh.

'You'd dump her, wouldn't you?'

'OK, Andy, if it makes you feel better, I admit I'd dump her.'

'So it's only fair. Why not tell her, Mikey?' I asked, trying to sound as calm as possible.

'Because we all know that it's 99 per cent likely she'll never find out.'

I had a brainwave. 'But let's suppose, for argument's sake, that you'd known ahead of time that your fling with Michelle was going to be caught on camera. You'd never have touched Michelle in the first place, would you?'

'Of course not!'

'So it matters, whether anyone's watching or not.'

There was a bemused silence for a moment. I seized it. 'Pete, I'm only changing the subject for a second – tell us, how old's your little sister Laura now?'

'She's four.'

'OK, this is gonna be gross, but hear me out. Just imagine some sicko middle-aged man interferes with Pete's kid sister. We corner him in a dark alley and we pin him against a fence. But he tells us that what he did with Laura felt like the right thing to do at the time, and that it was too good an opportunity to miss . . .'

'That's totally different,' Mikey blurted.

'I know, but just stay with me and I'll get to what's relevant. The fact is, our reaction to the sicko shows that we think there is such a thing as right and wrong. We couldn't care less if he enjoyed himself with Laura. Or that it felt right for him. What he did was just plain wrong. And if he'd done it with any four-year-old anywhere else in the world, we would have said it was wrong, even if the laws in that country said it was OK. Even if every person in that sick society said it was OK.'

'So what's your point, Dan?'

'My point is that we are convinced right and wrong exists.'

'Yep. So what?' Andy said.

'Where does that come from? And why are we so sure that some things are just plain wrong? Why do we get so worked up about these moral outrages? Could it be a clue that there's a source of right and wrong? That fits with the idea that God exists. And if God exists and has seen everything we've ever thought, said and done, then there aren't any secrets when we stand before him when we die. If that's the case, we needn't feel reluctant to do what's right. In fact, we'll be much better off doing what's right. We might even feel pleased to do what's right.'

Andy suddenly lit up: 'Hang on. Has Dan, the back-from-the-dead-man, got a point? He hobbles up the stairs and we happen to be talking about Mikey's tortured love life, and he shows us that whether God exists should make some difference to whether Mikey does the right thing or not.'

Pete interrupted: 'What? How do you work that one out then?'

Andy continued, 'It's simple. If there's no God, then good luck to Mikey the two-timer. If there's no God, Mikey should do exactly what he wants. There aren't any consequences beyond the grave because there's nothing beyond the grave. No truth, no consequences. So none of us can object to Mikey playing the percentage game. If he doesn't want to tell Anna the truth and thinks he can get away with it, then fine. We can't tell him he's wrong because there isn't any such thing as absolute wrong, only opinion. But if God exists and has seen the whole thing, then there's a positive incentive for Mikey to cut his losses and tell Anna the truth.'

We all looked at each other. Lots of sideways glances. Mikey seemed worried. Andy looked pleased with himself.

Mikey stood up. 'OK, Dan, you've got me interested. You know I can't resist a challenge. If you can prove to me that God exists, and that he saw me and Michelle, then for the sake of the argument I'll do the right thing. I'll confess all to Anna, and bring it all out into the open. But I can't imagine for a moment you'll be able to do it. And just in case you try, I want some evidence for God, as well as your experience.'

I went to the loo and prayed a sort of 'Help!' prayer. Pete went out to collect a pizza, and when he came back I gave it my best shot.

'Let's take a run-up to the God question and go back ten years. Think how much easier life would have been as a kid if your mum had believed that things happened for no reason whatsoever. Ribena spilt on the carpet – no problem. Tidy room trashed by muddy football boots – no questions asked. Plates and mugs broken, biscuits and cakes literally disappearing – that's life.

'But it wasn't like that. Not even once was it like that! When my mum came home to find the patio window smashed and a cricket ball nestling among the shattered glass, I pleaded total ignorance, but surprise surprise she wasn't satisfied. She passionately believed that things happen for a reason. I was grounded all summer, with all privileges withdrawn.'

'Where are you going with this, Dan?' Pete asked.

'Windows smash for a reason. That's because the whole of life revolves around cause and effect. So why should any of us believe that the universe began to exist for absolutely no reason? It's like saying that one day there was a vast empty nothingness, the next there was a carrot the size of Watford. A massive carrot would demand some sort of explanation.' Here I went into the stuff Rob had told me about how the universe had a beginning. I finished a few moments later by saying, 'The universe looks suspiciously real. Other real things have a reason why they started to exist. Why not the universe? It was caused. Perhaps it was caused by a God?'

'Mate, you're a long way short of getting me to re-organise my whole life,' Mikey said.

'Of course, it's early days,' I said.

The truth was I didn't know much more, but I was looking to quit while I was ahead. It was 1.00 am, with school the next morning. Pete gave me a lift home on the back of his bike.

chapter 3

I went back to Rob's after church the following Sunday. He showed me a photo of his girlfriend Megan. I couldn't quite believe Rob was a teacher. He had the same CDs as me.

'How did it go with your mates?' he asked, as I wondered what his relationship with the red-haired Megan was like.

'Mikey says he wants evidence.'

I told Rob blow by blow what had happened. He seemed excited to pick up the threads. 'Look up there,' he said. 'Think about the Americans putting a man on the moon. Neil Armstrong sticks his flag in the dust and looks down at our planet. He's looking at a phenomenon.'

'What d'you mean?'

'Well, it's common knowledge that if we were a bit closer to the sun we'd fry, and if we were a teeny bit further away we'd freeze, and if the moon wasn't exactly the size it is and with exactly the orbit it has, we'd be flooded by the tides.[3] But if you look further back to the earliest seconds of the universe's life, it's far more awe-inspiring.'

'You're talking about the Big Bang?' I asked.

'Yeah,' Rob said. 'The real challenge for Mikey is that it is so highly unlikely that anything should exist. Take the Big Bang model, for example, which I'd be happy to go along with for the time being.[4] Have you ever thought about how many different forces you needed to magically exist for no apparent reason on day one to get our universe? The real sensation is the relationships between them. The show-stopper is the ratios.'

'I don't get it.'

'Well, it turns out that there has to be the most exquisitely delicate balance of competing forces at the very start of the universe for anything to exist. Just imagine that it's true that once upon a time all the matter that currently exists in the universe was compressed into one tiny speck. Incidentally, where did that speck come from? The atheist has no answer. And then there was this thing called a quantum fluctuation. Why should such a thing as quantum mechanics exist? The atheist has no answer.

'Anyway, then there's this incredibly unlikely explosion, which causes all the matter to fly outwards but at a perfectly controlled speed. Too fast and nothing will ever settle down and exist in the universe. Too slow and the universe will never get going in the first place.

'So the universe expands, but the speed of expansion turns out to be critical. It's slowing down at just about the rate that it expands. If it slowed down too much the universe might collapse back on itself.[5] In fact, it's still got just enough juice to carry on expanding for ever. Which just happens to be exactly what's needed. How very convenient![6]

'And it must be our lucky day because the four fundamental forces of nature – gravity, electromagnetism, the strong nuclear force and the weak nuclear force – have all turned up right on cue. The fact that they go to all the bother of existing is another mystery. But then we find that they are perfectly interrelated and balance beautifully, like . . . er . . . a hippo tip-toeing on a tightrope right across Niagara Falls! In other words, not a sight you'd expect to come across unless something very clever were going on. One false move and it's all over.

'Take stars in the sky. They're held together by gravity, but at the same time energy flows out of each star by electro-magnetic radiation. To get our sun, for example, you have to have those two forces perfectly balanced.[7]

'What's more, the balance between strong and weak nuclear forces is cunningly precise. A tad less of the strong, and the whole universe would consist of hydrogen. A tad more of the strong and all the hydrogen in the universe would have converted to helium. Again, no good. Only a narrowly defined ratio will do.

'What about atoms? You've got to have atoms to have anything existing. Atoms need precise relationships between protons and electrons and neutrons. A proton is 1,836 times bigger than an electron, for example. A little messing with that number and the universe would never have formed.[8]

'Now here's my favourite. You've got to have slightly more matter than antimatter for the universe ever to have existed. If you have exactly the same amount of each they just annihilate each other, and the start of the universe would have been explosive all right, but you would have been left with next to nothing. On the other hand too much matter and the universe would have collapsed so quickly after the Big Bang that no planets, stars or galaxies could ever have formed.[9]

'Do you want me to go on?'

'Er, yeah . . . I mean, I don't understand the science but I get the principle.'

'OK, well, you can't have life on our planet without carbon and oxygen. They're created by burning hydrogen and helium inside stars. This is a bit complicated, but in the 1950s they discovered that a couple of percentage points difference either way in the reaction and carbon would never have existed. Carbon is a stunning shock development. We're carbon. So no carbon equals no us.'[10]

Taking a book from his shelf, Rob said, 'Here's what Britain's most famous scientist, Stephen Hawking, concludes about the staggering number of cosmic coincidences I've just described: "It would be difficult to explain why the universe should have begun in this way, except as the act of a God who intended to create beings like us." '[11]

My head was spinning by this stage, but I went back through it all again with Rob and made some notes. What was important was that I knew all this evidence would get me a hearing with Mikey, and then we could get onto what I really wanted to talk about.

chapter 4

Back at home things were going better with my mum, but my sister was becoming more and more distant.

I had started to have what's called 'quiet times'. At church they'd suggested I have a set time when I read the Bible each day. In fact I tended to have 'noisy times', when I'd sing very loudly and then read a bit of the Bible and then pray for people by name. Jesus was just as real in my bedroom as he'd been when I was dead, even though I couldn't see him. I found I was praying more and more for my sister Kate because things had changed between us – for the worse.

The Saturday after my visit to Rob's, a group of us went into central London on the train: Mikey, Anna, Andy, Pete, me and two girls I haven't told you about yet called Heather and Suzie. Anyway, as Andy was paying for the tickets, I was kicking a can around with Pete, and I spotted Kate, my sister. She hadn't seen me and was dashing for a train. She got a ticket out of her pocket, which she'd obviously bought beforehand. I'd never known her do that before. I set off to follow her.

Well, she shot down the stairs and there was some big bloke

at the bottom of the stairs and she gave him a hug and then they were off, straight onto a train. I ran down after her, calling out, but my injuries slowed me down with every step and I was left windswept on the platform all on my own, watching the last carriage pull away. Like a scene from a movie, except with a large McDonald's strawberry milkshake in my hand.

'What's going on, Dan?' Suzie shouted after me, jumping down the steps two at a time. 'You got us worried. Are you all right?'

'Er, yeah. My sister's got some new boyfriend she's not told me about. I just saw them.'

'Never! She'll want to choose her own clothes next. I'd give her a stern talking to if I were you!'

'Yeah, OK. He just seemed a lot older than her, and I suppose it looked a bit creepy, that's all.'

'Dan, she's 16. She not a baby any more.'

Suzie was right. I'd never been ecstatic about anyone Kate had gone out with. Andy used to be interested, and even that didn't settle too easily with me. But Kate and I had told each other everything up till now.

That evening, when Kate came in, I was on the phone telling my aunt Ruth about Jesus. I gave her the whole story. Unlike my mates, she seemed to accept everything I told her at face value. She even asked to come over the following day. Then I heard the door go downstairs.

'I'm ba-ack,' Kate called up to whoever was home.

Once I'd finished the call, I was straight downstairs.

'So who's your new man, Katie?' I asked, offering her the cup of tea I'd made for myself.

'What do you mean?' she replied.

'I saw you down the train station. I didn't know there was anyone new on the scene. I was just surprised you hadn't said anything.'

'What d'you mean? I went up London on my own.'

'Come off it, Katie. You'd even bought your ticket in advance. It's not a problem. I just thought I'd ask. What's his name?'

'There isn't anyone. Look, Dan, I went into town on my own. Perhaps you mistook me for someone else.' With that, she picked up the tea and went into her room.

Well, maybe I had. I mean, I'd only seen her from behind. But she was my own sister, and, no, it was definitely her. Why was she lying to me? It was totally out of character. Then again, if he was a lot older than her, she probably wouldn't want Mum to know. Kate was obviously not going to tell me the whole story.

The phone rang again. It was Mikey. 'Got Mr Foot all lined up for our next session, Dan,' he said.

Mikey's idea was that we'd talk about life, the universe and everything with Mr Foot, the physics guy, there with us. This suited Mikey because he'd be able to cross-check everything Rob had told me with Foot. I knew God was real whatever anyone said, but that wasn't where Mikey was at.

The following day we were in the lab. After sticking his head round the door, Mr Foot invited us into the science staff common room because there was no one using it. This was the inner sanctum, and I'm not quite sure why Mikey and I were allowed in. Well, it was a big let down – a dismal little room, pokey and horrible. They treat teachers like scum. They had lockers just like us. I thought it was embarrassing. We found a grimy corner. Foot tried to make himself coffee but couldn't find a clean mug.

Sitting down, notes in hand, I told them both what Rob had told me – all about fine-tuning. I got most of it straight.

'All that true?' Mikey asked Mr Foot.

'Yeah, bit sketchy, but not bad.'

'You agree with Dan?' Mikey asked.

'We're safest working from the known to the unknown,'

Foot continued. 'The First Law of Thermodynamics says matter can't create itself, and the Second Law says that matter decays or sort of winds down. So first, the universe didn't make itself, and secondly it's winding down. So it makes sense to say that it was once wound up. When the Big Bang theory hit the headlines in the 1960s it seemed to fit perfectly. So yes, I do think the universe burst into existence, and I've no idea why.[12] And Dan's correct that the odds are stacked against it. A man called Roger Penrose, who worked with Stephen Hawking to develop our current understanding of black holes, computed the odds of the Big Bang producing by accident our ordered universe as one in 10 to the power of 10 to the power of 123.[13] I've memorised that number because it's actually got more zeros on the end of it than the total number of particles in the entire universe. Those are massive odds to fight against.'

'But on the other hand,' Mikey said, 'maybe there were billions and billions of universes trying to come into existence, and the only reason ours exists is because our numbers worked!'

'Flipping heck, Mikey Walters!' Mr Foot cried. 'Why don't you ever come up with anything that bright during lessons? Did you think that up yourself?'

'No, I must admit I heard it on TV. What about it, Dan?'

'I haven't a clue,' I said, stalling for thinking time. 'What evidence is there that any of these hypothetical other universes ever existed?'

'None, Dan, but that's the whole point,' Mikey said. 'We can't detect them, but they could be out there.'

'But isn't it more scientific to draw our conclusions from studying the one universe we can observe than to speculate about other universes which as far as we know don't exist?' I felt this sounded convincing. I didn't know if it was.

Mikey clearly thought he was onto something: 'Look, Dan,

it's a well-known fact that if a monkey hits a keyboard at random long enough, eventually, given an infinite amount of time, he'll type out the complete works of Shakespeare. Isn't that right, Mr Foot?'

'Well, that would be my view, but I'm not sure you could describe it as a fact.'

Mikey pressed on: 'Dan, you've got to admit that's possible.'

I replied, 'I simply don't know. What I do know is that if you were reading anything as carefully crafted as Shakespeare's plays, and you had to bet your life on the author being either a monkey or a person, even you, Mikey, would bet on a person.'

'Gentlemen, I don't think you need me. It's all terribly interesting, but we shouldn't really be in here,' Mr Foot said, and we all got up.

'Mikey, do you really want to bet your life?'

A pause.

'What do you mean?' Mikey asked looking slightly fed up.

'If you'd booked a ticket on an aeroplane that had been scientifically demonstrated to have no more than a one in a million chance of landing safely, would you bet your life and get on it?'

The answer was obvious so Mikey didn't even bother responding. He was staring out of the window onto the playing fields we'd trudged round for the previous seven years, but I knew he was thinking about Anna, and the deal he'd done with us when we were all ganging up on him a week before. 'The stakes are pretty high, aren't they?' Mikey said eventually.

I replied, 'You heard Mr Foot – the numbers are against it. The chances of the universe just happening are practically zero. Do you really want to bet your life on something so unlikely?'

'It just grates with me, the whole religion thing.'

'Well, I was the same, remember, until the accident. Look, I'm still me. Let me put it to you another way. If we went down to the newsagent's right now and bought a lottery ticket, and then we found out next week that New York's top mafia boss had won, and we saw that he'd won again the following week and the week after, then after a few back-to-back mafia wins we would begin to work out that something was up. That the game was rigged. Mikey, the game's rigged,' I said with real passion. This was the first time I'd ever levelled with Mikey in my entire life.

He looked me in the eyes. It was almost Hollywood.

'The game's rigged,' I repeated. 'It has to be. There's just too many coincidences, too many precise equations, too much fine-tuning, too much evidence for a creator for you to say that God definitely doesn't exist. For all you know, outside of your current experience there could be a God you haven't come across yet. This God dreamed up the elegant laws of physics and rigged the game so that the universe could come into existence.'

Mikey was taking it on the chin. 'OK, but I'm not quitting,' he said. 'We'll carry on, but all I'm saying is that God . . . may exist. You've proved nothing yet. I'm only conceding a few inches, and you're never going to get me in a church, so just forget all that side of it. And don't give me any Jesus freak stuff or I'll pull the plug. Besides . . . even if you do prove that God's real, unless you get a nose job, I'll still be better looking than you!'

Throwing his pen at me, he'd defused the situation brilliantly. Thank God, the bridge between us had survived the strain.

chapter 5

Hi, my name's Kate. You probably know I'm Dan's sister. Well, I'm not too keen on all this God stuff. I mean, everything was fine, wasn't it? We were going along in the car, and then . . . wham! The accident that changed everything.

I still get headaches, and I lost four weeks in hospital and all that time at school, which I can't get back. I'm still struggling, and I missed out on the school ski trip, which is just about the only thing about our school that's any good in my opinion.

And then there's Dan. You try and make your brother as small a part of your life as possible, but I have to admit that Dan is OK, as brothers go. There's only the three of us in our family, and seeing as Mum and I are only on speaking terms about 50 per cent of the time, I need Dan to pull through for me.

But Dan doesn't. Dan goes and dies. All those hours of utter desperation, my mum and I bawling our eyes out kneeling on the hospital floor. He's dead. Why did he have to die? Why couldn't we all have died? Why Dan?

And then he's not dead! He flipping opens his eyes! So now it's jubilation, celebration, and everything's OK – until we discover that Dan's gone weird. OK, I shouldn't say 'weird' – different. It's all God this, God that, Jesus this, Jesus that. Now that's totally freaky, because we're not a religious family, and Dan's the last person, I'm not kidding, the last person I would expect to join the God squad. But this all happened to him *while* he was dead. I mean, whatever next?

I know you know all this, but it's pretty hard being me. All of a sudden there's this overnight change, and this person I live with wants me and Mum to become Christians – as if we're not already. Flipping cheek!

On the other hand, I have to give Dan some credit because he is a nicer person than he used to be. He's not as arrogant. He used to fancy himself something chronic, but he seems to have mellowed in that respect, and he is more considerate around the house, although that's not saying much.

As for all the religion, I admit I can't explain where he got it all from. Maybe he did experience all this stuff. Maybe he didn't dream it up. And maybe I am missing out. But I take the view that you've got to get on with life, and I'm certainly not looking to join the girl guides at church. I don't have much freedom, and I don't plan on giving it up.

Anyway, that's all the God stuff. Last month something else happened. Something you don't know about. Something Dan doesn't know about. It's got nothing to do with him or religion. It's the biggest problem I've ever had to face. I'll tell you the whole story in a few minutes' time. I'd be grateful for any advice I can get.

chapter 6

Dan here again. We're at a party, the music's thumping through the walls. I don't know whose house this is. We were told to say on the door that we were friends of Anna's. You know, Anna, Mikey's girlfriend. Funny thing is, Anna's not here, but Mikey is. I can see him across the kitchen, but there are so many bodies I can't get to him. We give each other a high five over everyone's heads.

'Dan mate, where have you been all my life? Anna's gone to the off licence. This could be our chance to talk,' Mikey says.

I sidle along a wall, and we start shouting in each other's ears, drum and bass deafening next door.

Mikey begins, 'Dan mate, you caught me on the hop the other day. I know what I want to say now – I've got my head straight. You've got me to admit that there may be a God who started the universe. At least, I can't rule it out. But I don't feel the need to do anything differently as a result, OK? Because as far as I know, God may have started the universe up and then gone missing. That doesn't mean I'm in any kind of trouble or that there's judgement after death. God might have nothing to do with life today. Besides which, evolution can explain the whole development of life on earth, and so there's no need to bring God in once the universe exists. I think that's it as far as I'm concerned.'

'OK,' I said, totally stuck for anything intelligent to say in reply, 'er . . . what if evolution can't explain the whole development of life on earth?'

'You *are* joking?' Mikey said.

I had no idea, but I had to come up with something.

'The survival of the fittest, mate,' Mikey continued. 'It's going on all around us right now. For example, look at this party . . . There's only two fit girls in this room: that one by the door and Sarah from the year below, who's over there by the corridor. Now what do you notice about them?'

'Surrounded by blokes.'

'Exactly. Welcome to planet life. Blokes naturally select the best-looking girls. It's the law of the jungle.' Mikey scanned the room, taking in the data. He pointed to a few girls talking among themselves in a corner. 'Look over there. Those wall-flowers aren't fit enough to survive in this environment.' This was a pretty brutal analysis, even by Mikey's standards.

On reflection, I'd been so excited about Jesus that I'd never gone back and thought about everything we'd been taught about evolution in biology. If every living thing could be explained by purely natural processes then why should Mikey believe God was involved? I knew there must be an answer.

'Seriously,' Mikey said, 'you should join us next weekend for the biology field trip, and we'll show you some evolution in action for one thing, and we'll finally get a few beers down you, for another. There's only ten of us in a minibus. It's in Wales. Middle-of-the-night skinny dipping. All good wholesome fun. You'd love it.'

I have to say that even though there was a world to win for Christ, I didn't want to quit on Mikey. He and Pete and Andy had been my best mates for years. Andy seemed interested by the change in me, though Pete was cautious. But I'd started something with Mikey that was going to be concluded one way or the other.

The following Monday, Mikey bounced up to me in the cafeteria. 'Newsflash – ugly English student accepted for dazed and confused biology larks in Wales. You're in, Dan! Williams says you can come. Bring a rucksack and some whacky baccy.'

Mr Williams was well known for being a bit more laid back than some other members of staff, and Mikey rejoiced in the fact that he could call him by his first name – Phil.

So after school on Friday I was off in the minibus. There were ten of us on board, and no one knew exactly where we were going. On the M4, Phil was on his mobile trying to work out the route.

This was my first chance to talk to Anna for two weeks. I tried to imagine what her reaction would be if she knew about Mikey's fling with Michelle Saunders. Yet she and Mikey looked so sorted together, holding hands on the minibus as we bumped along. She'd be devastated if she knew. But would Mikey ever tell her?

We eventually arrived at a farmhouse that had some sort of

accommodation block. We'd been on the road for six hours including a food fight at a Little Chef. I was shattered. I fell into the bunk-bed and decided to sleep with my clothes on – it was freezing.

The next day Phil announced the mission. Wait for it . . . snail collecting! Whoopee! In the last analysis, biology was deathly boring after all. OK, cutting up sheep's lungs with scalpels when you're twelve is fun for boys, but then it's one long downhill slide to a weekend's snail collecting at the age of 17.

To my astonishment, neither Mikey nor Anna seemed disappointed that we were now staring down the barrel of two days' tedium. We had another hour in the bus before we got to the coast. I followed Mikey down to the water's edge – we each had a bucket in hand. I felt like a complete prat. The waves crashed in on the rocks, spraying up into our faces. We could just about stand up in the wind. It could have been a romantic scene apart from the snails.

'Why snails, Mikey?'

'Because it's evolution in action, mate. Look at these.'

Over the next two hours, we found that exactly the same snails had different colour shells depending on where they'd camouflaged themselves around the beach.

'They've adapted to their environment,' Mikey said. 'But that's not all. When we go round to the next bay, we'll find the same snails, but the shells there are different again.'

I failed to see why this was so exciting.

'Dan, this is how all life developed. These snails made small adaptive changes to survive. If you're a black snail on a white beach, some bird is going to spot you a mile away and come and eat you. So snails adapt or die. And now their camouflage is genetically inbred. That's just the start. In the same way, millions of small changes over millions of years can turn one species into another. That's how all life developed.'

This was nothing new – it was only what we'd been taught. I looked back at the rocks, and then at Anna who was trying to do a handstand in the wind, laughing to herself out loud, though she didn't know we were watching. She then climbed up onto the rocks and looked out to sea. Anna was so full of life, which was why we loved her. But the rocks were just dead. There did seem to be a world of difference between non-living rocks and living things.[14]

That evening I raised it at the dinner table with Phil, Mikey and Anna there: 'How did the first living thing come into existence?' I'd made my question sound more threatening than it needed to be, and everyone looked up as if I'd just insulted their grandma.

'It evolved,' Mikey said, as if answering for the group.

'How?' asked Phil, being the typical teacher for once.

'Well, there were all sorts of chemicals bubbling around in a soup. That's what the early earth's surface was like, wasn't it?'[15] Anna said.

'OK, so let's assume that there were lots of chemicals bubbling around. How did anything living come to exist? How did we get the first living being?' Phil asked.

'The chemicals reacted with each other and made a few proteins which made a few cells. And then we were up and running. I mean, given enough time anything can happen,' Mikey replied.

'A few proteins made a few cells!' Phil said with the sort of mock sarcasm that I can only imagine teachers practise in the mirror every day before school. Yet somehow Phil carried it off without sounding tiresome and predictable. He was in his late 20s and had a goatee beard. Famed for hanging out with sixth-formers, I was finally getting to know him a little bit. Was he just playing devil's advocate?

'It's just a little bit more complicated than that,' he said. 'Just one cell is as intricate as a giant high-tech factory. On the outside you've got a security system which only allows exactly the right goods in. That's the cell membrane. Elsewhere in the factory you've got power sources in the cell cytoplasm which can be accessed by a central memory bank (the cell nucleus). The nucleus stores and retrieves vast amounts of information, decoding artificial languages at bewildering speeds. Raw materials are directed along miles of corridors, and precision quality control mechanisms prevent any slip-ups. But then the cell does something no high-tech factory ever does. You know?'

Blank expressions all round.

'It reproduces itself within a few hours.'

'Well, that's cool, but so what?' Anna said.

'So what? Getting all of that to exist all in one go is a pretty tall order, no matter how long you've got. So how could the factory have just happened?'

'Chance,' Mikey replied. 'Dan here getting a girlfriend is extremely unlikely, but given enough time even that's possible.'

Mikey was a great one for laughing at his own jokes, but I was totally zoned in on Phil, waiting to see where Phil was going.

Phil continued, 'To get the most basic living thing, the most basic cell, you'd have to have amino acids which just happen to exist and then of the many different types, you'd have to isolate the 20 amino acids which are usable for making proteins. Then you'd have to go through them one by one picking out only the left-handed ones. Then you'd have to assemble the amino acids in exactly the right sequence and join them to special peptide bonds that fold three-dimensionally, and if you hit the jackpot and got 100 amino acids in the right sequence you still wouldn't have life – you'd only have one protein. You'd need maybe another 200 or so proteins to even have the first sniff of a chance of life.

'Meanwhile, you'd have to ensure that nothing interfered

with your creation, because the chains of amino acids could be broken just as easily as you formed them, so you'd have to protect them somehow, and make sure nothing else reacted with them.'

I chipped in, 'You're talking as if the process would need a designer. Could it have happened by chance?'

'It must have happened by chance,' Mikey said. 'Otherwise we wouldn't be here today.'

'But could DNA have just happened?' Phil asked. I had no idea what his agenda was. He was keeping us guessing brilliantly.

I knew that DNA was something to do with our genes. It gave us either blue or brown eyes. It was recovered from crime scenes. I asked Phil, 'Look, I'm no biologist, so can you just explain what DNA is?'

'OK. Dan, you asked if the process of forming the first living cell would need a designer. Yes, it would. DNA is the design code. It's information,' he said. 'It's a code that tells the amino acids to arrange themselves in a special sequence, creating proteins. A longer stretch of code is called a gene. DNA is the code of life.'

'Can you keep it simple?' I interrupted.

'OK, Dan, I'm going to send you a text message from my mobile. I've got 26 letters plus some punctuation to choose from.'

I told Phil my number and when my phone buzzed, I picked it up. It read: 'AGGTTCTCCCAAGAGGTTCTCC-CAAG'.

'But that looks like rubbish,' I said.

'Stop being so hard on yourself, Dan. It's actually the shape of your nose.'

'My nose?'

'It's a code, Dan. It's a genetic code that your body under-stands and reads. And a much longer code like that determines the shape of your nose and what shape your children's noses will be. Let me send you another message.' Phil was texting away frenetically.

MAKE HIS NOSE LIKE BRAD PITT'S NOSE.

'Look at that. Think of all the intellectual concepts involved. I've just communicated with you through a code called the English language. I assume you can read the code. I assume that you understand what a nose is. That's what the A, G, C and T message was doing. Your body understands the AGCT code. And there's a film star in Hollywood who's carrying that message right now.

'Now let's imagine back at the dawn of time, billions of years ago, on a lonely planet there is a primitive soup all over the earth. No living thing exists, but for no particular reason all these amino acids happen to exist. But hang on, what's this? . . . Look over there . . . wow! There's a single-celled organism that's got a code in it! The code's telling the organism to select amino acids in a special sequence so that the organism can reproduce itself. And, oh my goodness, look now: the code works! The cell's just divided and reproduced itself! Isn't that clever?

'Now just how did the code come to exist? And how come the code can be understood? There's no reason why the ACGT sequence should make any more sense to the first cell than it did to you a few minutes ago! Where did the code and the means of translating it come from? They're both needed from the word go. One's useless without the other.

'So, to use the analogy of the text message, if I left my phone on the table for ever, it would never write and send you that message all on its own. Sure, the letters are there on my keypad, but that doesn't help unless we introduce some intelligence. But once I start texting, that's like the message telling the amino acids lying around at the beginning of time on the primitive earth what order to get into. You've got to introduce intelligence to get any sense out of the letters!

'In fact you need a lot of intelligence. A one-month-old baby could never send you a text message about Brad Pitt which is powerful enough to reproduce an attractive nose! If the baby could get the phone to work at all, she would send you random gobbledegook. DNA code must have an information source. The phone isn't the information. Did the phone think up the message? Of course not! The phone doesn't know what a nose is.'

'OK,' said Anna, 'this is all good stuff, but what's the point?'

'The point is that information-rich messages which can reproduce life don't just happen.'

Silence from the group.

'You're saying the first DNA message must have had some thinking behind it?' Anna asked.

'Precisely. When DNA arrives on the scene, it's an instruction book. That looks suspiciously like forward planning! So where did the first DNA code come from?'

Mikey was clearly becoming annoyed. 'I don't know,' he said, 'but one day science will lead us to the answer.'

'But Mikey,' said Phil, 'maybe science has led us to the answer. Let's think back to an amazing day, 28th February 1953, when Francis Crick walked into the Eagle pub in Cambridge and announced, "We have found the secret of life!" He'd just discovered the structure of DNA. Nobody knew what its structure was before, but Crick and his colleague James Watson had worked it out. And for the rest of his life, Crick insisted that DNA could not have just happened. It could not have been formed by chance.'

'Why not?' Mikey barked, bemused by the turn of events. 'Why can't the building blocks of life have just organised themselves and created DNA?'

'OK, look at this book,' Phil flicked through the huge biology textbook on the table in front of us. It was full of pictures of every sort of animal. 'Like the DNA code, this book is full of ordered information in a readable code.[16] What caused this book to exist? Was it (a) the work of an intelligent author, or (b) the result of a terrorist who blew up a printing press causing ink to fall on paper in random ways, which happened to create a whole book of sequenced meaningful English sentences? You cannot seriously expect me to believe that (b) is the best explanation? Crick and many other leading scientists today would say (b) is such a remote chance that it's no chance. And that it's non-sense.'

'My guess is still that the building blocks of life organised themselves and created DNA,' Mikey said.

'But that's like saying the ink on the page is the author of the book! You're saying the ink is intelligent enough to think up the storyline and then write the words, commas, sentences, and get everything spelt correctly! Ink can't do that . . . only an intelligent designer can do that.'

There was a stunned silence. Phil looked around nervously, as if he had just confessed to a murder.

'Mr Williams,' I interrupted, hardly able to believe my ears, 'you said an intelligent designer. Are you saying that you believe in God? That God made DNA? Have your studies led you to become a Christian?'

'No, far from it,' he said.

This was, of course, something of an anticlimax.

Phil continued, 'But there is now a growing consensus among scientists that life could never have developed on this planet by chance alone. At least, all chance theories are currently at a dead end.[17] Beyond that, I would take the same view as Crick. Perhaps life came . . .' more nervous glances 'from a spaceship.'

'What?' I shouted, hardly believing that this whole amazing discussion was going to end with something so random.

'I know it sounds far-fetched, but the difficulties involved in getting life started on this planet, and in particular the existence of DNA, have left me wondering whether life originated elsewhere in the universe and came here . . . I dunno, perhaps on a spaceship. At least that's Francis Crick's suggestion.'[18]

'The bloke who discovered DNA thinks life originated on earth as a result of aliens coming here on a spaceship?'[19] I asked incredulously.

'Er . . . yes.'

Although Anna had started laughing, she soon stopped, as Phil was obviously serious. It seemed that Mikey and even Phil Williams were prepared to go to any lengths to avoid a supernatural explanation for life. A few days earlier Mikey had been prepared to believe in an infinite number of hypothetical universes that could never be detected to avoid the conclusion that God might have created the one we've got. And now Phil Williams was saying that because the chances of life ever developing spontaneously on earth were now known to be zero,[20] undetectable aliens brought life here in a spaceship. These guys wanted God not to exist!

I was convinced that Phil must have reasons for refusing to believe in God. 'Phil,' I asked, 'wouldn't it be more scientific to believe in a God we can detect than in prehistoric spaceships we can't?'

'Yes, it probably would. But if I were to believe in God, I'd have to change the way I live my life, and I don't want to do that. I'm happy as I am.'

I saw my opportunity. 'But you haven't solved the mystery of life, and neither has Francis Crick. You've just moved the problem elsewhere in the universe. You know that life couldn't have arisen by chance here, but you've succeeded only in shifting the problem . . . to the planet Krypton.'

'OK, so it's not a completely satisfying explanation,'[21] Phil said. It was an astonishing understatement.

The group broke up, pretty stunned by the twist at the end of the evening's tale. Aliens! Gadzooks!

We picked up our plates and went to wash them up. Mikey walked slowly, deep in thought.

'Mikey, what about it?' I asked.

'OK, I'm still stuck,' he replied, 'but I'm not giving up. The case for God is a lot stronger than I thought. And in particular, DNA does look like it was produced by a "who" rather than a "what", so the intelligence is . . . a problem. I don't have an explanation for DNA, but I'll find one.'

'Maybe the explanation is finding you, Mikey! I'm not giving up either. God is the intelligence. He is real. And he loves you so much, he won't let you go. If only you'd let me introduce you to . . . the intelligence. You'd never regret it.'

chapter 7

At that moment, my phone went – a text message. I didn't pick it up at first because I was still on an adrenaline rush after our UFO trip. When I read it, I nearly fell off my chair: 'Mum's got a live-in boyfriend – ring me back – kate'.

She wasn't one for practical jokes. I went outside to get a better signal.

'Hey, Kate – it's me.'

'He's called Mark. He's here. He's in the . . . living room with his feet up on the table watching telly.'

'OK, calm down! Who is?'

'Mark. She's got herself a boyfriend, Dan. She's finally gone and . . . done it.'

If this was a wind-up, my sister must have been taking

acting lessons.

'Where the hell are you, Dan?'

'I'm in Wales.'

'Wales! Well, you'd better get yourself back here pretty sharpish because there's a middle-aged man scratching his you-know-whats in the middle of my life.'

'You're breaking up . . .'

I lost the call, but she'd said enough to convince me that it was for real. The minibus back to civilisation couldn't leave fast enough. Surely my mum hadn't really met some bloke and shipped him in to live with us? She'd never been with anyone since . . . well, Dad left when I was four, so how long's that? Thirteen years! She went on dates, but they were always disasters. She just didn't trust men. We'd occasionally see someone in a Ford Mondeo pick her up, but then she'd be home by 10.30 pm and we'd never hear of Derek or whoever it was again. She was a nun!

All the way home, I was thinking, 'Who is Mark? Is there really, honestly going to be a man living in our house when I get back?'

I rang the doorbell. I had my key, but I was too flustered to get it out.

Totally expressionless, Kate opened the door. She looked pale, like she does when she goes incommunicado on us. Kate believes in masses of conversation or none at all. She just raised her eyebrows, put one hand on her hip and with the other she pointed to the kitchen. With an exaggerated sigh she said, 'He's in there.'

I slowly walked into the kitchen, bracing myself. And there he was! Larger than life and twice as pretty, making himself, now let's see . . . some hot chocolate!

'Mark,' he said, thrusting out his hand. 'Bit of a surprise, I know! Look, I am really sorry. We didn't mean to spring it on you both, but let me try and explain . . .'

'Hi! I'm Dan.'

He looked familiar, but he definitely wasn't one of the Dereks who'd swung by in their Mondeos. Mark was probably older than he looked. He was probably about 50, but looked 40. One of those people who pay more attention to their appearance than you'd expect. What is there to prove when you're 50? But Mark obviously shopped around, because he'd got some decent gear on. He'd coloured himself beautiful on the basis that he was going grey. A bit like Gary Lineker, but only in as much as his grey worked for him. He was a bit more with it than Mum. Mum had sort of given up the ghost and let her figure go to pot. Mark was impressively slim. He had just a hint of aftershave, or at least enough to keep you guessing.

'Your mother and I . . . er . . . well, we met up recently, and we sort of hit it off, you know, and I work in Manchester, or rather my office is in Manchester. I'm an IT manager, and I'm on business here for this week, and your mum invited me to stay. And she's just gone out to buy . . . something.'

Kate called out from upstairs, 'Danny boy, she's gone out to buy some new sheets for their bed. It's not even funny.'

After half an hour talking to Mark, everyone had become a bit more chilled. Mum came home, and basically pitched it to me as a trial period. Mark would stay for a week and we'd all see how it went. Everything had happened so quickly and she just hoped we'd all get on. Kate was furious that we hadn't been consulted. I was happy enough, but couldn't see it working unless Mark could turn on the charm with my sister.

Anyway, all that was Sunday night. I put all my soaking biology field trip kit out on the radiator. What a weekend!

chapter 8

The next morning, we were off to school. We didn't drive any more. Not since the accident. I got the bus, and always left before Kate, who tried to arrive at the last possible minute.

Anyway, as I was having my crunchy nut cornflakes, out of the corner of my eye, I spotted a photo of me sticking out of a cookery book on the kitchen worktop. I went over to open it up and it was a cutting from the local newspaper. It was the story of the accident from a few months ago. It's a horrible picture, I look like low-life scum. One of those school photos that come back to haunt you. Of course I'd seen the story before, but it had a yellow post-it note stuck to it which said in block capitals: 'SANDRA – NOW YOU'RE ALL OK, CAN I SEE THE KIDS? I'LL BE IN TOUCH – DAVE.'

As soon as I saw it, I knew it was from Dad. We hadn't had any contact for 13 years. All Mum told us was that he was in New Zealand, and that was the postmark on the birthday and Christmas cards we got from him. Never any message, just 'love Dad'.

Dad had gone off with another woman, and left my mum with a four-year-old and a three-year-old. Apparently, Mum (Sandra) went ballistic and swept through the house purging it of every photo, video, book or anything else which reminded her of Dave. She even threw away her wedding album, which meant that Kate and I had to live this *EastEnders* story line whereby we couldn't remember what our own dad looked like. He had no other family. His parents were dead. And we had no photos of him.

Now of course that mattered. I had my idea of what he looked like. He looked like . . . and then it hit me. He looked like Mark! As far as I could remember anyway! Well, that's what people do, isn't it? They go for the same type again and again. Unless, of course . . . Mark was Dad!

No, that's ridiculous. Mark seemed totally genuine anyway. The whole idea of Mark really being Dave, my dad, was just too ridiculous.

But he looked like him.

At that moment, Mark walked in. It was the first time a man had come down those stairs in the morning for 13 years.

'Dan, are you OK? You're staring. I know I'm a bit of a novelty.'

'Sorry . . . er . . . Mark. Just takes a bit of getting used to.'

He looks like Dad. He really does.

He mumbled about the meeting he was going to, and tried hard to take an interest in my day, but I was already late for school. It was a shame that Kate was on the warpath because I was sure I could grow to like Mark.

Time to go or else I'd miss the bus.

chapter 9

It's me again – Kate. Look, Dan doesn't know what's going on, so I'll keep it brief. I am angry about Mark. But it's not Mark that I want to tell you about. It's true that I don't like Mark. Actually, he's OK. It's what he stands for that's bothering me. I can see Mum settling down with him, and I can't cope with it. Can you understand that? Is there anyone reading this who's been in this situation? It's not that I expect my mum to stay single for my sake for the rest of her life. Far from it. If Mark can cheer her up, then good luck to him.

I'm just hurting, 'cos I've had it with . . . men. And I'm taking a complete break. I just want you to know something incredibly personal about me. I need to tell someone 'cos I've been keeping it in too long already. I can tell you because you're only reading this and you don't know me and so you can't tell anyone, but my last boyfriend, Nick . . . well, we split up last month. We had a . . . you know . . . a sexual relationship, which was fine, but towards the end, he just got more and more into it, and I almost felt like one night, the night before we broke up, he . . . you know . . . he raped me.

Does that sound over-dramatic? It wasn't like a *rape* – like a rape on the ten o'clock news. Everything was normal at first, but . . . I just didn't want to do it that night. But he insisted. And since then, I've sort of kept it all in, the emotions and all.

But then, first of all it was Dan actually. Dan, driving me mad, constantly telling me how much God loved me. It really upset me, Dan going on and on about it. If God's so full of love, then why did he let Nick do that to me? Why all these traumas one after another? Why did God allow the accident? Dan's all excited about it, but I've still got headaches every night from it, and I'm still struggling to concentrate in lessons, and then why does Mum have to get a live-in partner right now? Just when I was trying to get myself straight? I don't want him living in our house. I don't want any man near me at the moment. We even have to share a bathroom. I mean – please! I just feel angry with Dan, with Mark, with Mum, with God, or whoever's in charge of this mess.

And I still have to see Nick every day at school and pretend I'm over him! I'm taking it out on Mark. I know that's unfair. It all just makes me angry. So now you know.

chapter 10

It's Dan here again. I was grateful for a dull uneventful day at school. Monday night is official video game night for our clique at Mikey's house. It's a sort of institution, so I needed to explain why I wasn't going.

'I'm seeing my teacher friend Rob Scott from church. You know – the Rob I told you about,' I said.

'Rob Scott?' Mikey asked. 'You didn't tell me it was Rob Scott. There was a Rob Scott who used to be mates with my brother Steve.'

'Well, I know Rob left our school about five years ago. I think he went to uni at Nottingham. Anyway, he started teaching at King Edward's in September.'

'It must be the same guy. I'm pretty sure Rob went to Nottingham. My brother's not mentioned him for ages.' Mikey was curious. He was obviously intrigued by the thought that one of his brother's mates had become a church-goer.

That night Anna, Mikey and I went over to Rob's flat.

'What happened to you, Rob? You disappeared off the face of the earth!' Mikey said.

'What happened to *you*? You were a twelve-year-old twerp when I last saw you. Now you're almost presentable! What have you done to your hair?'

Rob was telling the story of how he'd become a Christian while at university studying physics and biology. Mikey couldn't help himself and waded in. 'It's a conspiracy! Are you going to tell me that now you don't believe in evolution?' Mikey asked, goading Rob.

'It's not a question of belief,' Rob replied. 'Evolution on a small scale is a fact, if you're talking about variation within a species. You get different types of finches, different types of pigeons; we can breed endless varieties of dogs. You get adaptations.'

'Like snails adapting to their environment?' I asked.

'Exactly, or bacteria which develop immunity to antibiotics. I'd call all of that micro-evolution.'

Anna interrupted, 'Look, I may be the only one here being a bit thick, but I fail to see what all this has got to do with God. What's the connection?'

'I can only give you my story,' Rob said. 'When I was your age, I wasn't a Christian. I wasn't interested. Besides, the vast array of plants, trees and animals I was studying could all be explained by purely natural processes. It's what every biology student is taught. Once there was a single-celled organism, but over millions of years, with the help of mutations and natural selection, that little amoeba evolved into a fish, fish into reptiles, reptiles into birds, all the way up to apes into humans. God was sort of superfluous, an optional extra that wasn't needed.

'Like everyone else, I thought evolution explained everything, from nothing existing in an empty universe all the way to you and me being here talking. But then it became obvious that there were two major problems. During my first year at uni, it became impossible to believe that the universe popped into existence without a creator, and then in my second year it became impossible to believe that the first single-celled organism (or amoeba) could come to exist without intelligent design.'[22]

Anna replied, 'So you started wondering about God?'

'Yes, and I probably would have stayed wondering, smoking joints and talking late into the night and getting nowhere, but at that point I met Megan. She was questioning the underlying assumption behind all we'd ever been taught, which is that everything can be explained without reference to God. She suggested that it's a bit premature to argue that the entire range of animal and plant life can be explained by the theory of evolution when the theory can't even explain how life started in the first place.[23] So we thought, if evolution can't explain the existence of the universe and the origin of organic life, then why are we so sure it can explain the transformation of one amoeba into people?'

Mikey threw his hands up and stood up. 'But that's like asking, "Does the earth really go round the sun?" This is crazy!'

'Mikey, we just asked, "What do we know for sure? Why are we so sure that amoebas evolved into people?" When Charles Darwin put forward his theory of amoebas to humans in transitional stages, back in 1859, he knew that there would have to have been literally millions of transitional species. In other words, fish that had grown legs, but legs not powerful enough to walk on, or land creatures which had grown the beginnings of wings, but wings not yet big enough to fly with.

'Darwin said that if his theory was correct, some of these fossils would be found. Well, as you can imagine, over the past 140 years we've dug up millions of fossils, but what we actually find is nothing much where we'd expect to find the transitional fossils,[24] and then nearer the surface a vast array of life, but with all the species pretty much as they are today. It's called the "Cambrian explosion".[25] We don't find a steady development of one species into another.[26] The missing links are still missing.'[27]

'But that doesn't prove anything!' Mikey said. 'I think it's amazing that any fossils exist. I mean, you've got to have an animal buried alive and preserved for millions of years.'

'I agree the fossil record doesn't prove anything,' Rob replied. 'It just means that although we have masses of fossils, we don't have the transitional species.[28] We just have to imagine what they might have looked like. But the gaps in the fossil record have become such a problem that lots of biologists have abandoned Darwin's theory of gradual change altogether, and they've suggested sudden change. Species evolving into another so quickly that no fossils were ever laid down!

'That just struck me as hugely convenient – if the fossils aren't there, we'll just accommodate our theory to explain why they aren't there.'

Anna came in: 'OK, so you're saying that we should have found these transitional fossils by now, but by and large we now know they simply aren't there, so we've had to come up with a theory that would explain why they aren't there.'

'Exactly, and so it meant that Megan and I were still a bit short on facts at this stage of our search. We were just looking for some hard evidence for amoebas turning into people.[29] And we got even more suspicious when we read a book by a biochemist called Michael Behe.

'He asked, "Surely there are some mechanisms in nature that only work in their current form?" They can't work in any less organised transitional form. He uses this great analogy of the mousetrap. Just think about a mousetrap. It only functions with all the parts in place. You aren't going to catch any mice without the spring, for example. You need six basic things to come together at the same time for it to work at all.

'Behe says the mousetrap is irreducibly complex, and there are mechanisms in nature like the mousetrap which have to exist in their current form on day one to be any use to anyone. Like blood clotting, for example. When you cut yourself you've got to have blood clotting on the surface of the wound or you'd bleed to death. But Behe showed just how fantastically complex blood clotting is. You've got to have all these elements working all in one go for blood to clot, and if you get blood clotting too quickly we'd all have a heart attack and die.'

Mikey said, 'I don't get it.'

'The point is, these mechanisms look like they've been designed all in one go. We can't imagine at the moment how they could have come about by small successive steps.'[30]

'OK, so that's a mystery?' Anna asked.

'A mystery which deepened when we came to our next question, which was about mutations. How could we be so sure that mutations, which are very rare and almost always harmful, really were a powerful enough motor to drive amoebas all the way to people? For fish to develop lungs and reptiles to develop feathers, you need to have lots of mutations happening all at once. A mutation in DNA code is like a typing error. Typing errors don't often improve a message. So the whole thing is almost inconceivable.'[31]

'So you're saying that you don't believe in amoebas into people?' Mikey asked.

'All I'm saying to you is that the case is far from proven. It's not a fact like the earth going round the sun. We don't have the fossils to illustrate it. We can't even imagine how the transitional forms could exist, and genetically it's so improbable that if we didn't have a prior commitment to keeping God out of everything,[32] I doubt the theory would have so many supporters.

'It just meant that when Megan and I met Christians who believed in intelligent design, we didn't laugh at them. We didn't treat them like the madwoman in the attic, irrational and unbelievable. We thought, "The God hypothesis fits with the facts rather than contradicting them." If God exists, why is it so absurd to think that he might have made some grown-up mechanisms, like blood clotting, all in one go, or even grown-up birds and mammals?'

Mikey shook his head. 'But that sounds more like fairy stories than science to me.'[33]

Anna was more open. 'No, Rob's saying that chance can't

get us all the way from amoebas to people, therefore you need something that isn't entirely random, something like God?'

Rob replied, 'All I'm saying is that by our third year, Megan and I reached a point where intelligent design of separate grown-up species required less religious faith than the religious faith we needed to carry on believing that amoebas turned into people by chance alone.'[34]

Mikey wasn't impressed. 'I need a cigarette,' he said as he wandered out onto the balcony and closed the glass doors behind him. I saw him going down the fire escape to stand on his own in the garden. The doorbell rang. It was Megan. She came in the front door and sat down with Rob and Anna.

I went out to talk to Mikey down in the garden. He'd gone all distant again.

'So, partner . . .'

'Don't start, Dan. Just don't start.'

'OK,' I said, turning to go back in, but then Mikey said, 'Remind me how I got into this mess in the first place?'

'Forgive me, but you . . . er . . . you two-timed Anna.'

'Yes. What I mean is, remind me what conjuring trick you produced to make me promise to confess about my fling with Michelle to Anna. Remind me what God had to do with it.'

'OK, when we were back in your room, we said that if there's no God, then anything goes. Anything you can get away with is fair enough. If you can have some fun without getting caught then good luck to you. If there's no one home in the universe, no camera to catch you speeding, then you can do what you want without any consequences.'

'And what was the problem with that?'

'By your own admission you can't live with that philosophy. If it's OK for you to two-time Anna, it should be OK for her to two-time you. But you told us you'd chuck her if she had a fling with someone else. You're like the car thief who objects to his own car being nicked. Or a murderer who isn't too keen on getting murdered himself. Mikey, we all know that there are some things that are just plain wrong.'

'I remember all that, and so what?'

'If your world-view doesn't work in real life, maybe we need to consider one that does. If there is a God, for example, and he's given us our sense of right and wrong, then that makes sense of the moral outrage we feel at murderers, for example. It even makes sense of the fact that you know in your heart of hearts that you should confess to Anna.

'Besides, and more to the point, God is the best explanation for what we do agree on – the fact that you and I exist as real people having a real conversation in a real universe.'

Mikey relaxed slightly. 'Dan, let me be honest with you and tell you what I'm feeling, but don't get too excited because it's not going to be what you're hoping for. I admit that it was a mistake for me to say that God definitely doesn't exist. You're right, he may well exist somewhere in the universe I haven't been to yet. I don't know everything, and I don't have any other explanation for the existence of the universe or the existence of life. I grant you that both those point to a creator. I also admit that probably one of the main reasons I've been so keen on humans being accidental amoebas that happened to turn into people is that it's enabled me to do whatever I want and live as if God doesn't exist. It's got at least as much to do with that as it has got to do with science. But I still believe that a single-celled organism turned into you and me over millions of years.'

'So in all that, are you now saying you believe in God?'

'I'm saying that I . . . er . . . believe I need to do the right thing.'

From the garden, he looked up at Anna. She and Megan were inside, going through a photo album. We couldn't hear anything going on in there, but we could see Rob going into the kitchen. Then Megan got up to join him. That left Anna all alone sitting on the sofa, and us in the garden below watching her.

Mikey started to go back indoors. I followed him excitedly each step up the fire escape. And then, on the balcony, he stopped at the crucial moment, with his hand right on the door handle. 'This is stupid. Why am I doing this, Dan? Why am I about to risk losing my girlfriend?'

'Because facts don't cease to exist just because they're ignored.'

'What?'

'I'm giving you reasons for doing what you're about to do. Reasons for telling Anna. Reasons for behaving as if God exists. All I'm saying is that there's evidence for God. It's up there, Mikey,' I said pointing to the stars. 'And it's there, and there.' I span round pointing to the skyline, to the trees, to Rob's cat, which was perilously close to falling off the balcony, and then finally to Mikey's chest. 'The Bible says that there's enough evidence of intelligent design in the world around us for anyone to believe in God.'

I then plucked up courage to try a Bible verse on Mikey. 'The Bible says that one day, Mikey, you and I will stand before God, and there's so much evidence for intelligent design, so much in the creation around us which suggests a creator, that when we die and meet him, we won't have any excuse. That's Romans chapter 1 verse 20.'

'So God's going to nail me when I die for two-timing Anna?'

'All Romans 1:20 says is that when you die God's going to treat you as if he gave you enough evidence to believe he exists. And if he exists, and you know he does, Mikey, then you should do what he says is right. And even you know that the right thing to do is to go in there and tell Anna the truth.'

'Tell her now?'

'It's up to you, Mikey. This is between you and your Maker.'

He gripped the handle and clicked the door open, walked in, and closed it behind him.

I stayed on the balcony and watched. Anna stood up, but then sat back down again, looking worried. I couldn't hear what they were saying.

chapter 11

Of course I wanted to hear every word Mikey was saying. Was he really going to drop the bombshell?

But standing on the balcony, I felt like a peeping Tom watching through the glass doors. Then again, I couldn't just barge in on Mikey and Anna's grief when their whole relationship was on the line. My only option was to go home and ask Mikey for the full story the next day. It was 10.45 pm on a Monday night. I climbed down the fire escape and out through the side passage.

I spent the 15-minute walk back to our house praying out loud for Mikey and Anna. Then, turning into our street, to my horror I saw Kate walking home from the opposite direction.

'What on earth are you doing out this late?' I asked.

'I didn't realise it was a criminal offence,' she replied.

'It's eleven o'clock at night, Kate. It's not safe to be out on your own. Where have you been?'

'What do you care?'

'Of course I care, and Mum cares.'

'Mum's out with Mark. Mum cares about Mark. And all you care about is your new religion.'

'Hey, that's not fair. You know I care about you, Katie, and so does God.'

'Oh, God cares about me does he, Dan? Is it because God cares that he let my dad walk out on me when I was only three years old? Perhaps God enjoyed seeing me arrive at primary school as the only one in my class who couldn't even remember what their dad looked like? What did I do to deserve that, Dan?'

Kate was raging. Where had she been? She brushed past me, opened the front door, and marched straight up to her room. I followed her.

'Tell me, Dan, is it because God cares about me so much that he's left me fatherless with all these insecurities? And just when I'm starting to put it all behind me, this caring God throws in a car crash just to smack me around a bit. Now I've got headaches every day and I'm falling behind at school. Just look at all this work!' She pointed to history books and sheets of paper strewn all over her bedroom floor. She obviously wasn't coping. I didn't know what to say.

'Katie, I know it's hard to believe, but God's in charge and he is a God of love.'

'Oh, God's in charge, is he? So where was your loving God when this happened?' She grabbed a book lying open on her bed and thrust it into my face. There was a gruesome black and white picture of a Nazi death camp – emaciated bodies stacked sky high. A rubbish tip of human remains.

'This is what we're doing in history at the moment, Dan. The "Holocaust", they call it. Tell me, Dan, was your loving God in charge when Hitler was liquidating six million Jews? Go on, Dan, tell me he was in charge, and I'll sue him for being asleep at the wheel of the universe!' She flicked through the book, making sure I could see each appalling image of Jewish corpses in prison suits.

'Look at this picture of the ovens, Dan. The Nazis decided

72

it wasn't worth gassing babies and small children, so they just threw them alive into gutters of boiling human fat. They killed four million Jews in three years at Auschwitz. Tell me, Dan, did God go blind for three years? Maybe he couldn't find Auschwitz on the map? Perhaps he was trying to get there, but got stuck in traffic? Or maybe God was terribly upset about it, but couldn't do anything to stop it, because he's so useless. Or maybe he just doesn't like Jews any more, not since they killed your precious Jesus! Come on, Dan, tell me there's some great reason for it all. Tell me that these Jews will find out one day that it was all worth it. I dare you!'

I wasn't up to the challenge. I was sickened by the pictures she was showing me. What exactly did they prove? I eventually said, 'Look, I don't think you can blame God for everything. It's not that simple. Take famines, for example. There's enough food on this planet to feed everyone, yet thousands starve to death. So why don't we feed the starving? Because people are selfish, Katie. People do evil. That's not God's fault; that's our fault. God's given us free will. And if we want real freedom, we may have to suffer those who abuse that freedom, like Hitler.'

'Yeah, well look at this woman on her way to the ovens of Auschwitz. I expect she would have happily told God where he could stick Hitler's precious free will.'

'Kate, I'm not denying that there's evil in the world.'

'So God created evil?' she taunted, hands on hips. 'I'm getting less keen on him by the minute.'

'No, God created the possibility of evil. People do evil.'

'And you reckon that gets God off the hook? I'm sorry, Dan, you're talking ****.'

'OK, so you want a perfect planet, Kate?'

'I just think that if I was all-powerful and all-good, and I had all the time in the world, I would have come up with something better than earthquakes, famines, Hitler, Stalin and

. . . what's his name? . . . Bin Laden.'

I replied, 'But if you had all the time in the world, would you have come up with anything better than music, art, sport, sunshine, the Grand Canyon, friendship, sex and love?'

'Oh yes, life's a beach, isn't it, Dan? Tell me this then: God's supposed to be just and fair, isn't he?'

'Er . . . yes,' I mumbled into the carpet.

'Then at the very least, if there does have to be suffering, it should be evil people who suffer most, not innocent people. Yet what do we find, Dan? Poor children suffering while rich evil **** swan round in luxury. Where's the justice in that? I mean, I'm no saint, but I do try and treat people fairly. Your God can't even manage that! And if he can't match up to the standards of the average person's goodness, I don't particularly feel the need to fall down and worship him.' She threw her history book down in disgust. It was a ferocious attack, and every single point she'd made hit home. Every blow had me reeling. Kate was pain on fire.

A silence. We were both numb with shock.

'Game, set and match, Dan,' she said.

Foolishly I carried on. I wish I hadn't. 'Look, Kate, I'm not disagreeing with you. But just suppose there's a God. What do you want him to do? Perhaps you think he should have created nothing at all – the ultimate low-risk option. Or perhaps you think he should have made robotic people, who are just lifeless machines. No feeling, no pleasure, no pain – just metal. Another no-risk option.

'But God chooses to go for option three, an extremely high-risk alternative. In option three, God creates highly intelligent, spiritual beings like himself. Free agents who can make real choices, just like he can. But the moment he gives them true freedom, he risks the possibility that they might choose to reject him. Now, why on earth would God choose option three? We wouldn't expect him to, because he risks a world of pain if people rebel against him and each other. Why does he take the risk? What's there to be gained by having free will?'

'I'm sure you're going to tell me,' Kate answered, exhausted by her tirade.

'Love,' I said.

'No, Dan, please don't talk to me about love. Not now.'

'That's the only possible explanation though, Kate. Why else would God put himself and us through all the suffering?'

'You're not making any impression here, Dan. I'd just give up and admit defeat.'

'No look, Katie. There is a direct link between free will and love – you can't have one without the other. For example, just imagine you're going for a walk in the park and you see a couple arm in arm, obviously in love. They walk right past you on the path without even noticing you. They're in a world of their own. Now, as you look at them, you know that there wouldn't be any pleasure in it for her if she knew for a fact that he was being paid to be with her! The whole thrill of it for her is that they've chosen each other. He could have chosen someone else, but he chose her. That's why love is exciting. You can't have love without some degree of free choice.'

Kate was nodding sarcastically. 'And robots can't fall in love. So I'm supposed to be grateful that I'm not a robot?'

'All I'm saying is that if God is powerful enough to stop suffering and chooses not to, there must be a reason. There must be some reason why in his opinion it's worth allowing suffering. His reason is that he wants there to be real love in the world, and because he wants real love, that means he's got to give us freedom of choice.'

She just shook her head.

'Kate, just answer me this: what do you want more than anything else in the world?'

'Dan, that's not fair. You know that I want to be loved.'

'Exactly. You were designed to be in a love relationship, and you're experiencing all this pain because you're not in that loving relationship. You were designed to be in a loving relationship with God. You were made to love.'

'OK, but if God's made me to love, why did he try and kill me in a car crash?'

'If he jumped in to prevent every accident, then everyone would drive as fast as possible down the middle of the road in the sure knowledge of never hitting anything. Don't you see, Katie? You've got to think through the consequences of what you're asking God to do. Every single time God steps in so that real choices don't have consequences, he reduces our freedom, until eventually he'll end up having to jump in every other minute and we're reduced to being robots, with no free will at all.'

'I don't want to be a robot, but I don't want this pain either!'

'So, Kate, the only deal you'd accept from God is a world where you can enjoy total freedom to do anything you want, but with no possibility of anyone ever suffering the consequences. That's like holding a gun to God's head and saying, "God, the only thing you can do to prevent me pulling the trigger is to create a round square." Kate, not even God can make a round square. Not even God can make a world where we enjoy real freedom but never suffer any of the consequences of our actions.'

For the first time, she went quiet. I should have stopped there, having just made my first decent point. But it was too late.

'OK, Dan, watch this!'

She stood on her bed. Throwing her head back, and thrusting her hands straight up into the air, she shouted at the ceiling, 'OK, God, this is me – Kate Adams. If you do exist, then show me now! Give me more than ancient detective stories and weird near-death experiences! Make this bed collapse! Shake the house! Let me fly up to the sky and shake your hand and congratulate you for finally doing something!' She stood to attention for a moment, and then cupped one hand condescendingly to her ear. The night silence was deafening. 'There you are, Dan. Nothing. Absolutely nothing.'

'But Kate, why should God be your slave? Why should he do party tricks just because you say so? If he did, we'd take him for granted and treat him like a dog.'

'But if God won't give me a modern miracle, then if he's got any power at all he should at least take away all the pain.'

'But Kate, pain is a warning sign that danger or death is coming. The process of dying is painful. So to take away all the pain, God would have to take away death as well. And no death means immortality. You're asking for heaven, and that's exactly what God is offering!'

'Dan, I couldn't care less about a hypothetical heaven, which may or may not exist. I'm living a real life here and now with real hurts, and I'm only interested in what's got real relevance to my life.'

'Look, Kate, if you're basically saying that life's a bitch and then you die, then in a sense I agree with you.'

'You do?'

'I agree with you – if this life of suffering is all there is. But if God exists and we live on beyond death in heaven, then everything changes. Looking back, this life will seem no more inconvenient than spending a single night hugging the toilet compared to forever in bliss.

'And God does know something about real pain. If you're asking, "How can God bear all the suffering?" well, he has. He did 2,000 years ago when his Son Jesus was tortured and executed on a wooden . . .'

'Oh Dan, for **** sake! Give me a break.'

'He watched his only Son suffer and die. God has suffered.

He came right down into the middle of it, and got crucified. And now he offers us heaven. A paradise none of us deserves, but the invitation's there for you and me. Kate, God isn't forcing himself upon you. He loves and respects you too much for that. He loves you enough to give you the freedom to choose.'

'Oh, does he? Then answer me this, Dan. Why did God value my ex-boyfriend Nick's freedom more than mine when he allowed Nick to rape me?'

It was a dreadful, horrible, utterly shocking moment. Nick Bailey . . . raped her? Her ex-boyfriend? I wanted to kick his head in. Not very Christian, I'm afraid. I also felt a surge of self-loathing. I was appalled at my own insensitivity. How could I have been so stupid? Now it was obvious where her anger was coming from.

'Kate, I am so terribly sorry. I've been a complete idiot.'

She burst into tears. 'What freedom did I have when Nick pinned me down? Why does God value Nick's freedom over mine?'

This time it was a question without an answer. She slumped down on the bed cross-legged and reached out her arms towards me. I was crying too. I gave her a big hug, but it was all too late.

chapter 12

Hi, my name's Anna. I guess you want to know what happened between me and Mikey. Well, what's the worst conversation you've ever had? Just hold that thought, and let me tell you . . .

He just walked in through the glass doors, and I was sitting there on my own – in someone else's flat for goodness' sake – and he said: 'Anna, I've got something I need to tell you.'

I stood up. 'You're scaring me. What?'

'I've done something awful, Anna. I don't deserve you. I never did. And I don't think there's any way you'll ever be able to forgive me.'

'What? What are you talking about?'

'Anna, I've been unfaithful to you.'

I didn't believe him. I thought it was another one of his pathetic jokes. But his tone of voice was frightening me. On sort of dazed auto-pilot, I said, 'Mikey, I can't cope with this.'

'I'm being totally serious.'

I still didn't believe it at first, but it was the expression on his face that did it. He looked . . . humble. I'd never seen that in him before. The colour was washed out of him. He hung his head, and then it hit me – he wasn't clowning around.

'Seriously?'

'Yes.'

He might as well have stabbed me in my stomach. I let out a scream. 'You . . . you ****!'

I got up to hit him with both fists. I wanted to punch him into the floor. But when I got close enough, just the sight of him disgusted me. He wasn't worth it.

(I'm told that Rob and Megan came in from the kitchen at this point to see what was wrong. I don't know what Mikey said to them, but they both scurried out again. I crumbled into the sofa and keeled over to one side. Burying my face in a cushion, I just screamed.)

'Anna, I know I can never make it up to you, but I want you to know that I really . . .'

'Who?' Suddenly I wanted to know with a passion – with everything within me.

'Anna, if you'll just let me explain . . .'

I stood up and slowly walked towards him, jabbing my finger straight in his face. 'Who?'

'Look, Anna, I know you're angry. You've every . . .'

'It's someone I know, isn't it? That's why you won't tell me, you little ****.' At the top of my voice, I yelled, 'TELL ME WHO!'

He didn't even have the courage to look me in the eye when he finally said it: 'Michelle Saunders.'

'You sick, sad ****! You choose the biggest **** in the whole school. When?'

'Exactly a month ago.'

'Where?'

'Anna, you don't want to know.'

He repulsed me. He was right, I didn't want to know, because he was already history.

'Get out of my sight!'

Thankfully he was most of his way to the door. Somehow, watching him slope off made me feel slightly better. I felt as if I was purging myself of something. Like the satisfaction you get when you finally squeeze a spot. I was wiping some pus out of my life.

He was about to close the front door behind him, when I was gripped by a strange curiosity. I called out, 'Why now, Mikey? Why tell me now? You're the sort of shallow **** who'd try and hide it from me. Why wait a month and then confess?'

'Because . . . I dunno. Because Daniel Adams has been messing with my head. Because I've been so selfish. Because all my life I've been acting as if there's no God. Because God is probably God. Because . . . I dunno. I don't know what's happening. I'm so sorry.'

And that was it. The end of me and Mike Walters. But that last bit – that wasn't normal Mikey. Fumbling around with Michelle Saunders was the sort of thing blokes like Mikey did.

But the staged, premeditated set piece confession with nothing to gain and everything to lose – that didn't make sense.

I spent two seconds thinking about it, and then all those feelings of rejection crashed in again. Something had been ripped out of the inside of me.

The slam of the front door had been Megan and Rob's cue to come back in. They must have heard every word. Megan gave me a cuddle. We cried together. Rob went chasing after Mikey, flying down the stairs. I just didn't care.

chapter 13

Flippin' heck! It's one thing after another at the moment. Sorry – this is Dan again. I've spent the week fighting my desire to knife a little kid at school called Nick Bailey, who date-raped my sister.

Of course, I've totally blown it with Kate now anyway. There she was, trying to tell me that she'd been raped, but was I showing any compassion? No, I was pouring acid on the wounds by arguing with her like a complete jerk.

Poor Kate. If only I could turn the clock back. I desperately want to undo what Nick has done to her. But she's been violated by him.

Looking back, I remember that when she was going out with Nick, I didn't think it was that intense. Then again, it did end pretty suddenly, but Kate told me she'd simply lost her respect for him. That was a clue, wasn't it? But I had no idea. And when I saw her with that big bloke at the train station, I assumed she'd put it all behind her and started going out with someone else, someone a lot older. Poor Kate.

So I've failed my sister. And since becoming a Christian, this is the first time I've really failed God big time. I'm struggling at the moment. I was trying to introduce Kate to the most wonderful relationship imaginable, but I've succeeded only in driving her to distraction. She won't go to the police, by the way. So it's a disaster.

But then again, since she's confided in me we seem to be a bit closer. In fact, right now we're out together late at night at the skate ramp with some of the usual crew: Andy, Pete and Suzie.

Mikey's depressed after getting dumped by Anna, so he's locked away in his room watching DVDs and won't come out. As for me, well, it's weird sitting here on top of this ramp, because this is where we always used to spend summer evenings. We'd sit up here smoking roll-ups and putting the world to rights. But then I had the accident, and while I was in hospital the council renovated the whole area and now it's all different, and I am too.

For example, the others are off getting some lagers and I'm waiting for a mate of mine from church called Nathan to meet me here. He's Alan Meadowcroft's son. Do you remember the lorry driver? Well, Nathan is Emma's brother. Emma who died in the same car crash as me.

In fact, here he is now.

'Hi, Nate.'

'Wotcher!'

As soon as Kate, Andy, Pete and Suzie came back with their cans, I introduced them to Nathan.

'So how do you two know each other?' Pete asked.

'We're part of the same church,' Nathan replied.

'Great,' Pete replied.

'You interested in church?' Nathan asked without any hint of embarrassment.

'No, it's not for me,' Pete said with a slightly nervous wink.

'Sure it is. You should come along and give it a go.'

Pete looked around saying nothing, obviously deciding whether or not he was going to choose this particular moment to speak his mind. We hadn't had a proper chat since that night when Mikey first told us about Michelle Saunders.

He eventually said, 'Look, I know that Dan here and Mikey have been having lots of deep and meaningful chats searching for truth. But I'm just not interested. I'm happy enough as I am. I'm 17 years old. I've got the looks and I'm surrounded by beautiful women and ugly blokes.'

Suzie had always been ever so slightly flattered by any attention from Pete. She said, 'Dan, it's all got very deep between you and Mikey. Anyway, no one knows for sure about any of this stuff.'

Pete again: 'Look, Dan, on the positive side, me and Andy were blown away by your story – you know, your life after death experience – but I'm not looking for a religion. I'd be quite happy to call off the search for truth. I've got my own truth and it's in the air, it's in my heart, it's – I dunno – in the trees, it's . . . it's in this can.'

With that he sprang up and drop-kicked his empty lager towards the bin below. It was always a competition as to who could get closest. Pete's can brilliantly chinked all around the rim and then right into the bin. We all cheered, as Pete threatened to take off his shirt and do a lap of honour.

'When you're as sexy as I am, you don't have to worry,' he said.

Suzie continued, 'Anyway, you don't have to go to church to be a Christian. I mean, I don't ever go to church, but I believe in God. God's in each one of us. We're all part of God in some way. We need to just connect with the God in all of us, and accept ourselves as we are.'

Pete jumped in: 'My attitude is, whatever works for you is

fine, as long as you don't impose your own views on other people.'

'What do you mean, Pete?' I asked, knowing full well what he meant, but I just wanted to get him talking.

'Well, what's right for you, Dan, isn't right for me. And what's wrong for you isn't wrong for me. There's no such thing as absolute right and wrong.'

'Are you absolutely sure?' Nate asked, not being deliberately cheeky. 'Haven't you just contradicted yourself?'

'How d'you mean?'

'Well, on the one hand you're saying that there's no absolute right and wrong, and on the other you're saying that there's at least one thing which is absolutely wrong and that's imposing your own views on someone else.'

Suzie was energised by this. I wondered if she fancied Nate. 'So tell us, Nathan: how do you tell the difference between right and wrong?'

'On the basis of what God says. How do *you* decide what's right and wrong?'

'By feelings,' Pete jumped in. He was rising to the challenge. 'The Bible's fine for you, but it's not really my scene. I go by feelings.'

'So what's moral and what's not?' I asked.

Pete replied, 'You don't have to believe in God to be moral. I reckon the world would be a much safer place if we just kept God out of it. What's moral is what you feel good after and what's immoral is what you feel bad after.'

Andy, who'd said nothing so far, chose this moment to ask something I wish he hadn't. 'Would that also be true of a rapist when he's finishing off a violent rape?'

My heart sank as I looked at Kate as subtly as I could. Of course no one else knew her situation, but to my relief, rather than getting up and walking off, she seemed totally gripped by the discussion. She hadn't batted an eyelid.

Pete said, 'Of course not. Rape is totally different. It's obviously wrong.'

'Not by your definition,' Nate said, again without sounding annoying. How does he get away with it?

Pete carried on, 'No, but if the general feeling of society says something is wrong, then that makes it wrong. There's safety in numbers. You don't need to bring the Bible or God into it.'

'But Pete,' I said, 'the general feeling of millions of Germans in the 1930s was that Jews were a menace to society. Does that mean that it was right to be racist in that culture?'

Pete said, 'Look, let's just call time out on this for a second. I'm only saying what most people in this country believe, which is that you don't have to be religious to be moral. And you can ask anyone. It stands to reason.'

I replied, 'I totally agree. But when most people in this country are shown a picture of Auschwitz concentration camp, it does more than just affect their feelings. Their reaction is more than "Auschwitz – yuk". They believe that some fundamental moral law has been broken.'

Nate was in my slipstream: 'And when most people in this country hear about a rape, they don't feel, "Well, that's her tough luck." They believe rape is absolutely universally evil. They believe that a moral law has been broken.'

'So what?' Pete asked.

Nathan had reached the moment of truth: 'Pete, there's no denying this moral law exists. Where could it possibly have come from?'

'This is a trap, isn't it? I'm supposed to say "God", aren't I?' Pete replied.

And then like a beam of light on a cloudy day, Kate spoke. She said, 'Dan, I hate to admit it, but I'm beginning to think you're right.'

'I am? What about?'

'Look, everyone,' she said with a theatrical flourish, 'the other night Dan and I had a blazing row. I was basically wiping the floor with his new religion, saying that a good God who allows evil can't exist. But this conversation is making me realise that you can argue it the other way too.'

You could have knocked me down with a feather. I wasn't sure if Kate was for real.

'What are you on about?' Pete asked. 'I must have missed something.'

Kate said, 'Well, I've been thinking about it all week. Why do I feel so strongly that rape and the Holocaust are wrong – absolutely, totally, globally, morally wrong with a capital W? Why am I so angry with God for allowing them? The answer is that these things really are evil. It's not just that I feel they're evil. They're evil whether I think they are or not.'

Pete: 'I'm sorry. I'm still in the dark here. Help me.'

Kate said, 'It's what Andy said that swung it for me – when he said that a rapist feels good after a violent rape. That proves that feelings are a rubbish guide to what's moral and what's not. And you can't just go by the consensus in society, because if society is racist that doesn't make racism right. And that's the **** irony of it, Dan, because it was Nazi racism and rape which were the two examples that I pummelled you with.'

I was nervous that Kate was about to accidentally tell the group she'd been raped. I didn't know whether she really wanted to do that. But she veered back from the edge just when I was afraid she was going to say something she might regret.

Pete said, 'Well, I'm delighted that you feel so enlightened, Katie, but I'm still seriously committed to having a good time and not getting drawn into this God thing that everyone else finds so interesting. I still don't understand it anyway.'

Nathan said, 'It's simple. The only way you'd ever end up describing a line as crooked is if you'd previously seen a straight one. Evil is that crooked line. And our repulsion at the thought of rape and racism is a clue that we're comparing these crooked acts to a straight one. And that straight line goes through all of our hearts, whether we like it or fight it. And if there's a straight line or a moral law in everyone's hearts, then where did it come from? Did it just drop out of the sky? Surely it makes more sense to say that God created it? Seeing as this law exists, the chances are there's a law-giver.'

'I can see it now,' Kate said, clearing her throat. 'If there's no God, then evil isn't a problem anyway, because there's no such thing as good and evil – just feelings. But evil flippin' well does exist! . . . So, and I can hardly believe I'm saying this, the reality of evil must be just as strong an argument for God's existence as it is an argument against it!'

'OK,' Pete said, 'this is all very clever and impressive, but I'm just going to say one last time that you're writing off millions of people who aren't part of Dan and Nathan's born-again brigade but still behave morally.'

Nathan said, 'I'm not writing anyone off. Of course there are people who aren't Christians who behave more morally than many of us Christians do. And that's to our eternal shame. But Pete, can't you see the principle? For example, imagine if you took a wrong turn late on a Saturday night in the city centre, and ended up stuck at the bottom of a dark alley surrounded by brick walls. And then you heard footsteps behind you. If you turned round to see six huge blokes walking towards you out of the shadows, you'd be terrified because you've got nowhere to run. But Pete, I've got to ask: would it make any difference if they said they'd just left a church Bible study?'

Nate had judged the moment perfectly. We all cracked up.

'All I'm saying is that we can all see there's a connection. The guys from the Bible class have got reasons to act kindly towards a stranger. Strictly speaking, if there's no God, there's no reason to act morally, especially if there are no police around.'

Pete kicked the heels of his Nikes into the ramp, trying to think of what to say next. 'OK, you say there's a moral law in all our hearts, whether we like it or fight it. Well, I'm a fighter. Nobody's gonna tie me down.'

Nate replied, 'Pete, God doesn't want to tie you down. He wants to set you free.'

'That's more like it.'

Pete and Nathan shook on it. It was pitch dark. Time to go. We all got up and said our goodbyes. Kate dragged me up and asked for a piggy back home.

'What about my injuries?'

'Isn't your God supposed to heal you? Tell him to hurry up.' Digging her heels in as if I was a racehorse, she jockeyed me home.

chapter 14

I just about carried Kate back, and after a brief chat with Mark, who I still can't believe is living with us, I finally went to bed. Since then I've been grateful for a quiet 24 hours. The main excitement was church youth group last night, which was fantastic. I told them how I'd slipped up and that I couldn't see how I'd ever be able to forgive Nick Bailey, and they all prayed for me.

You have no idea how good it feels singing worship songs to God. It's totally different from anything else. The only thing that comes close is the camaraderie you feel on the dance floor at a club right at the very end of a session. But that's just a temporary high, and it doesn't go anywhere. This is a real connection with God. You actually feel his presence. How cool is that?

Kate's no longer at all-out war with Mum and Mark, although it's not exactly the end of hostilities. They are discussing peace terms, and I've been called in to decide how much territory she's going to be given upstairs.

Anyway, the morning after church youth group, I was on my way out when I got a text from Anna asking whether we could meet at lunch. My battery was low, so I decided to charge it for ten minutes before leaving home. I couldn't find my charger, but eventually tracked it down in Mum's bedroom. The reason for all this detail is that when I knelt down to plug it in, I saw a note under Mum's bed, which looked as if it had been deliberately hidden. A second later, I was reading:

Dear Sandra,

I know this is breaking all the rules, but it's been 13 years now and I'm back in the UK. Please give me a chance. All I'm asking is that you meet me, just once. And if we can't work something out then fine. If not for my sake, or even yours, then for the sake of the kids, please ring me on 078111 743201.

Dave.

I was in tears. This was the longest piece of handwriting I'd ever seen from my dad. I'd wondered whether he was still alive at times, and whether Mum paid a stranger to send us birthday and Christmas cards from New Zealand just to string us along. But now, here was proof that Dad was interested in us. After all this time! So why hadn't Mum said anything? Had she just ignored this letter? No, she would have thrown it away. Maybe she'd rung him and met him. But why not tell us what was going on? Perhaps because Kate had always said that she hated Dad for walking out on us, and wouldn't ever want to meet him. But why keep it quiet from me? I looked at the date on it. It was six months old. That was about when Mum first met Mark! At a trade fair in Manchester, he said. Was this IT manager really Dave, my dad? Maybe he had a passport, or something else that would prove who he really was. I sprang to my feet and started rifling through the drawers. I just had to find something, anything . . .

'Dan, what on earth are you doing?' Kate burst in through the bedroom door.

'Looking for . . .' I was afraid that telling Kate what I'd discovered would tip her over the edge, 'my phone charger.'

'It's over there in the socket. What's going on?'

'Thanks. I'm in a rush.' My mind was racing. Maybe Mum had decided the only way to get Dad back with Kate was to move him in as someone else! And then, when both Kate and me had grown to like Mark, she was going to tell us who he really was!

But no, I must be going mad. Mark was just some bloke. He wasn't leading a double life. He had told me about his brothers and sisters and a hundred other things that couldn't all be lies. I decided to say nothing to anyone until I was sure of myself.

chapter 15

Later at school, Anna came up to me in the lunch queue.

'Dan, I've got something I need to tell you.'

Not another confession, surely?

'The truth is that I used to be really into God,' Anna said. 'It began at this camp I went on when I was nine. In fact, it was the biggest thing in my life for ages. But then by the time I was about 15, I'd discovered, you know . . . life, and then God totally drifted out of my thinking, right up until Mikey told me that he had a friend in hospital who'd gone all religious overnight. And just listening to you and Mr Williams and meeting Rob and Megan, and then what happened with Mikey, well, it's sort of stirred it all up again.'

Pete then bowled up and Anna immediately changed the subject, as if she'd be embarrassed to be caught talking about God in public.

As we chatted about nothing, I was tapped on the shoulder. I turned round and a girl I'd never seen before handed me a note. It said: 'My mate fancies you. Meet me at the bus stop after school.' I looked up to see Kate and all her friends burst out laughing. I think they were looking for a bit more of a reaction. Kate came over. 'Seriously, I do want you to meet me at the bus stop. I need to show you something.'

chapter 16

'Where are we going, Katie?'

'Shut up and walk.'

I always tried to do what she said, within reason. It made life so much easier. I said, 'Look, I just want to apologise again for the other night. I was bang out of order. You know how much I want you to get to know Jesus, but I acted like a complete idiot. I was a bad example of a Christian to you, Katie. Please forgive . . .'

'That's OK. Last week I went ballistic at Mum and Mark too, so you're not the only one who's been in the firing line. Anyway, I've been thinking some more about suffering. In fact that's why we're going where we're going.'

'Where are we going?'

'Wait and see. In the meantime, I was thinking in geography this morning: how are you going to excuse God for things like earthquakes? You were ever so keen to tell me that most suffering is caused by selfish people, but earthquakes have got nothing to do with people.'

As it happens, Andy had asked me the same question, and I'd asked Rob how he would have answered. I said, 'As far as I understand it, earthquakes are caused by plates on the earth's crust rubbing together. But if we didn't have plate tectonics, or whatever it's called, then the different continents of the earth would erode into the oceans and there would be literally no life on earth.'[35]

I was in the process of trying to explain myself, when Kate interrupted: 'Not good enough. Besides, in any case, my suffering is still pointless, isn't it? Don't get me wrong, since that night at the skate park I can now see how you can argue from evil just as easily for God's existence as against it, but suffering is still random, isn't it? And it serves no purpose. And it doesn't look like there's a loving, protecting God behind this world.'

'I agree it doesn't look that way, but sometimes appearances can be deceptive.'

'How d'you mean?'

'Well, when I was a kid I thought the dentist's was a torture chamber. All facemasks and needles. I was forced to go in there, then he held me down in the chair, and I screamed with pain as this man in a white coat drilled into me. The more I screamed, the more I thought he was enjoying it. As far as I was concerned, he was attacking me.'

'So what?'

'Well, I had no idea that the pain was actually worth the gain. That's because I had a kid's perspective on pain. What if we're like the kid, and God's the dentist? For all we know, a loving God might allow some suffering because he's actually doing us a favour. Life can be like that, can't it? I mean, we've all gone through painful times only to realise years later, looking back, that we've learned something good through it.'

Kate was trying not to walk on the cracks in the pavement. 'At the end of the day, I don't want pain. I want freedom. I don't want anyone cramping my style.'

'OK, well there you go. If God kept every teenager in the world indoors on a Friday night because he wanted to protect them from the pain of hangovers and broken hearts, there'd be a global riot! But people all over the world are grateful for the freedom to go out at the weekend. Perhaps equal doses of freedom and suffering are needed for us to become mature enough to enjoy life to the full.'

I had been reluctant to even talk to Katie because I was nervous about upsetting her again. I wasn't sure how much of the conversation she was really taking in, as she was obviously focused on where we were going. But we seemed to be just wandering aimlessly through the streets around our school.

Then she suddenly went for it again: 'So the point of my suffering is . . . what exactly?'

'Well, take our car crash, for example. Looking back, what's its effect been? You've been angry about it and I've been happy about it, but in both our cases, the car crash made us think about God in a way we never would have done otherwise. It burst our bubble of taking life and God for granted. It woke us up.

'Just imagine, Katie, if the events set in motion by that crash result in you becoming a Christian. And because of that you spend the whole of eternity in paradise. If that happened, you'd have to conclude that your suffering was far from pointless!'

She replied, 'But you're creating an afterlife to try and compensate for the injustices we suffer here. That doesn't prove heaven exists; it just shows that your system doesn't work in this life. So inventing another one doesn't solve anything.'

'I've got other reasons for thinking heaven exists.'

'Well, I reckon that when you're dead you're dead,' she said, 'though it does bother me that people are getting away with murder.'

'Getting away with murder?'

'Well, people like Hitler should have something coming to them beyond the grave. At least, that makes sense of how I feel. So I don't like the idea that people like him have got away with it. They commit suicide and then they're just like everyone else – nowhere.'

I replied, 'But if Christianity is true, then murderers aren't getting away with anything. They were on about this at church two weeks ago. Justice delayed is not necessarily justice denied. Saying that Hitler's got away with it is like storming out in disgust halfway through a film, complaining that the director should have given the villain his just deserts. You've just walked out before seeing the end of the story.'

'You're talking about hell?'

'Exactly,' I replied. 'It's a place where no one is let off more lightly or punished more harshly than they deserve. Does that make any sense to you?'

'Well, it might do.'

'Well, don't you think it's interesting that most Christians have had their faith strengthened by suffering? If the fact of suffering was such a knock-out argument that it actually disproved the existence of a Christian God, then why don't more Christians quit? Why does suffering have the opposite effect?'

Kate had stopped behind me. She was standing in front of Pete's front door.

'This is Pete's parents' house. What are we doing here?' I asked.

'Wait till we're inside.' She got out a key.

'Where did you get that from? What if someone's home?'

'Trust me,' she said.

We went upstairs. I was used to turning left into Pete's bedroom. Instead, we turned right into Pete's sister's room. In huge wooden multicoloured letters on the door, it said 'LAURA'. She's only four, as I think I told you ages ago.

I had no idea what had possessed Katie to take us first into Pete's parents' house, and secondly into their daughter's bedroom, and then she said: 'Dan, this is where it happened. This is where Nick raped me. Right here on this four-year-old girl's bed. It was Pete's party. We went upstairs. There was another couple in Pete's room, so we ended up in here.'

She started to cry, and I felt powerless. I just don't know what to do in this sort of situation. I didn't know whether to touch her. I didn't know whether to say anything. I was nervous I'd say the wrong thing.

'I've wanted to come back here for ages, because I think it's the only way I can put it all behind me. I just want to see this room without Nick in it. I want to see it all pure and innocent like Laura is. I want closure on all this, Dan, and I started to get it that night at the skate park. Someone mentioned rape and I didn't freak. You are helping me, Dan, in your own strange religious way. I've been thinking to myself that if I could just come over here and stand in the room and say, "This is a normal room. What happened here is in the past. Everyone else has moved on," then maybe I could too. So you're sort of moral support, because you're the only one who knows, and I thought I might collapse if I came here alone. I made up a story about losing some earrings to get the key off Pete.'

She sat tentatively on the bed.

'So what are we going to do?' I asked.

'I dunno. I just want to sit here till I've got it all out of my system.' She opened up her bag and got out her history textbook.

'You're going to do homework?' I asked incredulously, wondering how long I'd be standing in Pete's sister's bedroom.

'No, I'm going to tell you right here, Dan, on the very bed where I was raped, what conclusion I've come to about suffering.'

I wasn't expecting this. I sat down next to her. Kate's right hand was shaking, like those old people in homes.

'That night when I told you about the rape, when you left my room I prayed out loud for the first time in my life.'

I was astonished. 'You did?'

'Yeah, but you won't like my prayer, 'cos I didn't use the Bible to pray from; I used this book.' She opened up her history course book again. 'I don't know whether the Bible's true, but I do know that this book's true. I started with that picture of the woman at Auschwitz concentration camp. I turned the page and looked at photos of the disabled, and of women forced to sell their bodies. Then a businessman, whose son had been abducted and killed by a friend. Next a black man swinging from a tree, lynched by the Ku Klux Klan, and finally an Iraqi medical doctor, whose son had just been blown to pieces in Baghdad.

'And as I turned each page, I made up a prayer as I went along. Out loud I said: "God, if you exist, and if Dan's right that one day you're going to judge me, then I want you to know that the only God who's got a right to judge me is one who comes down into this world of garbage and knows what it's like to be a hated Jew. A God who cares for paralytics and prostitutes. Who's innocent of any crime, but gets betrayed by a friend. A God whose son is executed by a prejudiced jury without a fair trial . . ." I just kept turning the pages, Dan, and praying whatever the pictures brought to mind. I said, "The only God I can believe in is one who dies a horrible and violent death through simply trying to make the world a better place." And then I realised that . . .'

I interrupted, 'That's exactly what happened when Jesus . . .'

'Yeah Dan, I'm not stupid.'

'But that's amazing!'

'Well, it wasn't exactly what I was expecting. So for once in my life, maybe – only for the next five minutes though – I'm open. My life was ruined on this bed, and I don't want to leave this room till I've at least begun to make some sense out of it. So go on, do your stuff. This is your chance. The clock's ticking. Say whatever Christians say about . . . about this.' She picked up a plastic crucifix that she'd accidentally sat on. I guess Laura played with it. It was pink, pretend jewellery. Kate just looked at it. It had a sticker on it which said 'Barbie'.

'Well Kate, guess what? I did some praying too that night after our scene. I lay on my bed and said, "Lord God, my sister's right. It is a problem that you created a world where it was either certain or probable that evil would happen. And God, why are so many people's lives nasty, painful and short? But at least you had the honesty and courage to take your own medicine. Whatever game you're playing with your creation, you've kept your own rules and played fair. You were born in poverty and died in disgrace. I've been a complete prat this evening, Lord. I've spent the whole night trying to get you off the hook for suffering, but the simple fact is that you put yourself on the hook. You put yourself on the cross."'

Kate was totally zoned in, utterly focused. She said, 'And there I was next door, staring at these Auschwitz pictures, saying that the only God I can accept is one who knows first-hand what it's like to be an innocent Jew, who's tortured and executed. I was so annoyed when I realised that there you were sleeping peacefully in your room believing exactly that.'

I now felt relieved to have another chance to talk to Kate. I'd messed up so badly the first time.

She asked, 'So the answer to suffering is?'

'A person. It's not really an answer as such. It's Jesus. Ultimately I don't think that lots of words are going to help you, Katie. Ideas and concepts are not what you're looking for, because you've got a personal problem, and therefore you need a personal answer. But as it happens, God is a someone, not a something. When we think of the worst moments of our lives, Jesus has been there. Are you broken? He was broken. Are you rejected by your friends? He was rejected. Are you hated for no good reason? He was hated for no good reason. When we cry out and complain that we can't take it any more, we can think of Jesus being killed on the cross, crying out, "My God, my God, why have you abandoned me?"'[36]

Kate seemed surprised that I'd stopped. She said, 'So that's it? That's the explanation?'

'Well, Jesus is more than an explanation. He's a person. I don't know if you'll ever find, in this life, an adequate explanation for what happened here. But I do believe you can leave this place with something more satisfying than an explanation. You can leave with Jesus. When all's said and done, something evil happened here on this bed. But something evil happened on a hill outside Jerusalem in about AD 30 when Jesus was murdered. And God brought something beautiful out of that. God allowed the suffering of his own Son, because he knew that through it something wonderful could be achieved. At the time, Jesus' disciples thought it was a disaster. Their superhero had been executed, and all their hopes and dreams were in tatters. But they had no idea that through dying on the cross Jesus was solving the biggest problem they had. He was solving the biggest problem I had and the biggest problem you have. And hey, I've been waiting six months to tell you this, Katie, so I just hope I don't blow it, but the reason Christians make such a big deal out of Jesus' death on the cross is because it solves the problem of . . .'

At that moment, Laura walked in. Her four-year-old face went pale with shock to see us both sitting on her bed. She froze.

'It's OK, Laura, they're my friends, remember?' Pete said popping his head round the door. 'Hi guys. Kate, did you find whatever it was you lost?'

'Er no, actually, but I found this.' She gave Laura the plastic cross. 'We'd better go.'

I couldn't believe the timing. I was just getting to the climax and then Laura walked in.

'She's so innocent, that girl – so pure,' Kate said as we wandered back out onto the street. 'I just hope some bloke doesn't mess her up. Look, Dan, I still feel the need to ask why. I still feel that God should have stopped Nick from doing what he did to me.'

I replied, 'Of course you do, and do you know what? All through the Bible people ask God, "Why is this happening to me?" In fact, we had this amazing night at church last month, all about this bloke called Job. God allows him to suffer one disaster after another. He's on skid row, in absolute agony, and then he asks, "Why me, God?" and he never gets any explanation.'

Kate sneered, 'Well, a fat lot of good that is.'

'But at the very end of his life, he does meet God. God turns up. God comes to him, and somehow that satisfies him.'

'How d'you mean?'

'Well, isn't it like Romeo and Juliet? As long as Juliet is with Romeo she's happy. What lovers really want is not rational explanations, but just to be with their lover. Juliet doesn't need a complete answer 'cos she's got a satisfying relationship with someone who loves her unconditionally. Katie, God loves you unconditionally and he proved it by his Son dying on the cross.'

Right then, Michelle Saunders, of all people, came round the corner. She nearly bumped into me. It was the first time I'd seen her since the revelations about her and Mikey.

'Mind out,' she said, as if I shouldn't really be alive.

Then there was a wolf whistle behind us. It was Pete, running down the road to catch us up. We got on the bus together and climbed to the top deck. Pete was staring at Michelle out of the window as if she was a celebrity, which she was in a way. Anyway, Kate then started bad mouthing her. The moment had gone.

chapter 17

It's me – Anna – again. You know how when you split up with someone it takes about two months before you can think straight? Exactly right. Did I hate him? Really hate him? Yes. Did I love him? Yes.

I was constantly replaying in my mind the rows we'd had – thinking of all the things I could have said, should have said and would have said if I'd thought of them fast enough. I'd lost a lot of arguments with Mikey, but I never lost a rerun.

And then as I was sitting there in my bedroom, on a Saturday afternoon, staring at a chemistry book, taking nothing in, my mobile went. It was Kate, Dan's sister, saying she needed to show me something straight away. And she wouldn't tell me what it was over the phone. Well, that got me worried. Sort of shook me up a bit. What could be so important it couldn't wait? She wanted me to go over and meet her at Megan's flat. And that was strange too. I didn't know Kate had even met Megan. Megan's 22 years old, remember, doing teacher training. I guess Dan had introduced them.

As I was walking to Megan's, I was looking up at the clouds, thinking to myself that I hadn't been really happy for nearly two years. But why? Most of that time I'd had everything I wanted. I'd been popular at both my schools. I'd had a string of boys who'd been interested in me. I'd had three boyfriends in those two years, who were, with the exception of Mikey, good guys. There was Tim-nice-but-dim, Adam, who was gorgeous, and then Captain Arrogance himself. But even when everything was fine with Mikey, I wasn't entirely satisfied.

Even on the very night Mikey first kissed me, when I should have been walking on air, I can remember lying in bed later thinking, 'There's got to be more to life than this.' I'm still stuck with that thought. There must be something wrong with me for feeling this way. After all, I've got a great family. I get on with all of them. My dad's promised me I won't have any money worries at university because his business is going so well. We go on great holidays. I've got masses and masses of clothes and stuff. I'm doing well at school. If I get my act together I'm sure I can travel. I've got great girlfriends. I can talk to them about anything. There's always loads to do. I'm never bored. Except I am. I am bored. Why?

And then I asked myself, 'When was the last time I was consistently happy?' Well, I guess it was when I was 13, when my social life, which seems pathetic now, revolved around a church youth group. But by the age of 15 I'd drifted away from church and I hadn't really thought about God since.

Now how did that happen? Well, the only way I can explain it is that being 14, for me anyway, was like when you're a kid and you think, 'If only I could have that bike, then I'd be happy.' And then when you get it, there's no pleasure in it any more. And so you aim for the next thing, thinking that will push all your buttons, and a month later, that's no good either. Well, when I was 14, I just wanted to get accepted into the in-crowd at school. And then when boys started noticing me, I realised that my goal was in reach. I reckoned that if people thought I was fun and cool, then I'd be sorted like the rest of them – satisfied.

But I was still supposedly living for God. So for a whole year, till I was 15, I had this ridiculous double life. I had my Christian friends at church, where I'd act Christian, and then I had my school friends, where I'd act just like them and do all the things they did at parties and whatever, and then one day I realised that this was stupid. I can't have two lives. So that was the end of me and God.

But as I was walking over to Megan's I realised that since the day I turned 14, I'd been seeking one buzz after another, and none of them had delivered as advertised. Why? Why at 17 was I still so insecure, worrying what people thought about me? Why did I even care what they said about me? Why was I convinced that despite what anyone said, I had a face like the back of a bus? Why was I always worrying about something when there was nothing to worry about?

And what did I leave behind when I was 15? Was it just innocence? Childhood? Can I ever have it back? Was that God thing real or was it just what I'd grown up with? My parents believe it all. So does Megan, and she's not stupid.

When I arrived at the flats, the main entrance door was open, so I didn't ring. I went straight up the stairs, and when I got to Megan's door, it was ajar, so I just pushed it.

'Hiya! It's me – Anna.'

And then I stopped cold. There he was. Mikey. Standing there in that jacket I used to wear.

Kate came in from the kitchen. 'Anna, this has all gone wrong. I didn't know Mikey was going to be here. He just turned up a minute ago, hoping to talk to Rob, but Rob's not here.'

I didn't need this. It was tough enough seeing Mikey across the dining hall every day. Now he was within spitting distance. I was tempted. Ignoring Mikey in the most blatant way I could, I said, 'So what's going on, Kate? Now I'm here, what have you got to show me?'

Kate looked flustered. She looked at Megan with an expression that said, 'What do I do now?'

I sensed something was up. 'Come on, I know it must be important. You're hesitating because he's here, aren't you? You weren't expecting him and now he's here that's thrown a spanner in the works, hasn't it? Whatever you've got to show me has got something to do with him, hasn't it? Come on, what is it?'

Kate got an envelope from her Lonsdale shoulder bag. She looked pale. Mikey looked even more vacant than usual. And then Kate got a photo out of the envelope and gave it to Mikey without saying a word.

Mikey looked at it and seemed to sink. He closed his eyes and bowed his head. He mumbled, 'Dan said something like this might happen, but it was just . . . you know . . . an example. It was part of what he was saying about how God sees everything. He meant an imaginary camera. God's camera.'

Mikey kept staring at the photo, which I couldn't see. The suspense was killing me. I was about to grab it for myself, when he said, 'Anna, I know you're not speaking to me, and after this you probably never will, but I want you to know that I'm very, very sorry.' With that he gave the photo back to Kate and walked out down the stairs.

'Give it to me then,' I said, beside myself with frustration. But I wasn't prepared for the surprise. It was a photo of Mikey and Suzie locked together, arms round each other.

'Suzie!' I said in disbelief. I threw it on the floor. I looked down at the photo lying there on Megan's carpet. It really was like being punched in the stomach. 'Suzie! I can't believe it. Suzie as well!' I said picking up the photo again. 'Where did you get this?'

Kate said, 'I got my photos developed today, and I was walking along the pavement going through them, and there were about four shots I didn't recognise. I remembered that Suzie borrowed my camera last month, and then I came across this one. I guess someone took it without her knowing. And I thought that if it were me, and if I'd been going out with Mikey at the time it was taken, I'd want to know. And seeing as I was coming over here anyway, and Dan told me that you'd really hit it off with Megan, I thought it was a good idea. Look, Anna, I've made a total cock-up of this, haven't I?'

'No, no, Kate. You're fine. I'm just a bit stunned. I mean, Suzie's a friend. You know, like a proper friend.'

I'd been furious about Michelle Saunders because Mikey had shattered all my dreams with someone so plastic, but now after a week of being single, I was trying to close down emotionally. I felt numb and cold about Suzie. She wasn't the type. Or was she? This was planned, calculated deception on a massive scale.

I sat down on Megan's sofa. 'You must be getting sick of the sight of me,' I said.

'Not a bit of it,' Megan replied. 'I'm chuffed you guys feel you can come over. I don't really know what to say.'

The next two hours were spent in endless cups of tea and a few tears. It helped just to talk to them, and it seemed that Kate had got some problems of her own, though I reckon she didn't give us the whole story.

Megan did open up. She said she'd been abused as a child by an uncle who stayed the night after a wedding. Hearing that sort of put it all in perspective. I mean, what a nightmare! Can you think of anything more horrible? I was so impressed, though, with the fact she could talk about it. It's obviously affected her whole life, but it didn't seem to be an open wound. I was convinced that her faith, or whatever Megan had, was real. She seemed to be able to cope, sort of supernaturally.

I said, 'Look, Megan, I think I'm at a bit of a crossroads at the moment. Not even talking about Mikey and all that for a second, I feel there's a hole inside me, and whatever I try and stuff inside it, I'm still left feeling dissatisfied. This is probably music to your ears, isn't it?'

'Well,' Megan replied, 'from a Christian point of view I can relate to what you're saying.'

'Something's wrong, isn't it?' I asked.

'Well yeah,' Megan replied.

Kate interrupted, 'This is what Dan was banging on about, or at least what he was leading up to the other day.'

I said, 'I just think lots of things are starting to come together for me at the same time, or maybe lots of things in my life are collapsing together. First of all, I've got this prolonged sense that something's missing, but I've also had these doubts all the way along the line that I've never really owned up to.'

'Doubts about what?' Megan asked.

'Well, Kate probably doesn't know this, but my parents are proper Christians like you, Megan, but I rejected it all. And then, sort of totally unrelated to that, to my amazement I found a subject at school I really enjoyed . . . biology. I was actually good at it. And when I saw how they explained everything without even referring to God, well, that sort of finished church off for good. That was when I was 15.

'But just in the last few months, I've been having these doubts. I could never have talked to Mikey about them, 'cos he's so proud, but I looked in the mirror one day and asked myself, "Am I really just a sack of chemicals?"'

Kate said, 'Come again?'

'You know, the whole way they teach biology is that there might as well be no God. But it just didn't make sense that at the end of the day my whole life was no more significant than say . . . a burp. But I used to try and give myself a slap round the face by saying, "Anna, that's life . . . that's evolution . . . that's your tough luck, chick, for being the meaningless product of a universe that looks like it's designed but actually isn't."'

They laughed. I carried on because I'd never said this out loud before and it felt right.

'But then we got into this debate on the field trip in Wales, and even the teacher admitted that life couldn't just be one big accident. And then Rob told us how you, Megan, had been through the same thing.'

'Well, that's right,' Megan said. 'It was almost a religious faith we'd had in atheism. And we'd been coming to all the evidence with our minds already made up. Then Rob and I met Christians at a time when we were unexpectedly open to hearing an alternative explanation, which, to our surprise, seemed to better fit the facts.'

Kate said, 'Well, I don't do science, but as I told Dan the other day, I've never had any problem believing the world's here for a reason. To me it's obvious, but I've had a massive problem believing that God is good. "If God's really there," I thought, "he should come into this mess and suffer a bit himself." And then I realised the other night, perhaps he has, through Jesus. But I don't know where to go next. I mean, how does it become, you know, personal?'

Megan said, 'I think you two have come by different routes to the same conclusion. Something's wrong. Something's missing. Something about life doesn't quite stack up. You're hurting because you're missing out on a relationship that we were all created to enjoy – a relationship with your Maker, who loves you unconditionally.

'How can I explain it? Sometimes I ask myself, "Why did my parents want to have me?" They wanted to have me because they wanted a relationship with me. They would have been severely cheesed off if after all they'd done for me I'd just deserted them and never seen them again. They would have loved me whatever I did, but they wanted me to choose to love them back.'

'So?' Kate asked.

'So God's like a loving parent. He's made Anna and Kate in the hope of having a love relationship with you guys.'

'But it's not happening, is it?' Kate asked.

'No, it's not,' Megan replied, 'because of things like this.' She picked up the photo of Mikey and Suzie. 'Mikey's been caught on camera, but the truth is that all of us have done things wrong. Maybe not as tacky as in this photo, but wrong nonetheless. Before I became a Christian, someone put it to me like this: "What if every single day of your life had been captured on video without you knowing?"'

Megan pulled a tape out from the bottom of a pile on the floor, dug out the remote control from down the back of the sofa and hit play. A home video came up on the screen, with crummy crash zooming in and out upon a teenage girl. When she came into focus, it was Megan. She looked a lot younger.

'This is my eighteenth birthday party,' she said. 'It's the only day of my life I've got on video, but I won't even show Rob the whole tape 'cos I'm so embarrassed by what happened at about midnight. But let me just put the question to you the way it was put to me . . . what if every single minute of every day of your entire life had been taped without you knowing? And what if the camera had the ability to record every word you've ever spoken, everything you've ever done and everything you've ever thought? And how would you feel if your friends saw a video of your top ten worst ever thoughts?'

I looked at Kate. We were both sobered up by this, because it felt real. No one said anything for the longest 20 seconds you can imagine.

Megan broke in, 'I think it's gone quiet because we've realised that we've fallen short of our own standards. So how much more have we fallen short of God's? Life is not just some absurd free gift left on the doormat with no note. It's been given us by God. And when you and I die, quite under-standably he's going to ask us what we did with it. He's going to have a tape of our whole life – thoughts, words and actions.'

'Flippin' heck,' I said. 'Are you sure?'

'Well,' Megan said, 'there won't actually be tapes, but there will be books.'

'Hang on,' said Kate. 'This is what Dan saw beyond death. This is what he told us in the hospital. It's all coming back to me. I can see him there in the ward telling us. It frightened the life out of me at the time, though I didn't let on.'

'Are you being serious, Megan?' I asked.

'Well, don't you think it stands to reason? I mean, when I die, can I honestly look God in the eye and say, "Let me into heaven. I deserve it!" Of course I can't. I don't deserve heaven. I don't deserve an eternal paradise. The Bible says that heaven is a perfect place. There's no imperfection there at all. And that means if I'm ever going to get in there, I need to be forgiven for what I've done wrong.'

'You mean our sins?' I said.

'Er . . . yes,' Megan replied. 'Ugly word, but it makes total sense. None of us is perfect, we've all done things wrong, and it's our sins, those things we've done wrong against God, that cut us off from him. The relationship's broken.'

'You're saying that's what's missing?' I asked.

'Yes. Sin brings separation from God and that's why you're not in a totally satisfying relationship with God.'

Kate said, 'You're saying that the reason we're alive is because God wants to have a relationship with us . . .'

Megan interrupted: 'That goes on for ever.'

'Whatever,' Kate said. 'But that we've blown it, by being selfish. So when we die, we stay separated from him for ever, a sort of eternal death. And here I lose the plot because this is where you go into this crucifixion business, right?'

'Exactly. The real surprise is that rather than God leaving us separated from him, he comes down as a person into human history, and takes all the punishment for our sin that we should have got. He dies on the cross instead of us. He takes the death and separation we deserve, and we get the heaven he deserves. We swap!'

'Really?' Kate asked. 'Is it that simple?'

'Well, did you see that Mel Gibson film *The Passion*? Well, the reason the cross is such a big deal is that it deals with the universal problem of sin,' Megan said. 'And I can tell you for a fact, the moment you put your trust in Jesus, the barrier of sin is removed and that relationship with God goes online. It goes live. There's love coming thick and fast. It's life-changing. And that's what's happened to me, Rob and Dan. That's what happens when someone becomes a Christian. You enter into this new relationship. Guys, that's what you're missing. That's what you're looking for.'

There was a minute's silence. Not because anyone had died, but because me and Kate were thinking about it. It sounded too good to be true, but then again it didn't sound cheesy coming from Megan. Megan was authentic.

Kate was chewing it over. She walked over to the window. Without turning round she said, 'Funny thing is, Megan, you making sense of Jesus makes me wonder what the other religions are on about. I mean, I can see that sin is a problem if you're trying to get into heaven, but what's so special about Christianity? Don't all religions lead to God?'

chapter 18

So, we meet at last. I've got no excuse, by the way, for what I've done. At this moment, I'm on my way to see someone I was in awe of as a kid. I respected him because he was a hard man. He was a drinker. He was a player. Now he's a teacher. And he's a Christian. And I don't know how that happens to people. His name's Rob, and my name's Mikey. And I'm in trouble.

Looking like a pervert, I've been hanging around a school playground. As it happens, Rob's teaching at a rival school to ours. I've only ever come here for football matches before. After 15 minutes of hiding behind a tree with my eyes glued to his car, I've intercepted him.

'Mikey! You frightened the life out of me,' Rob said as he dropped his car keys. 'What are you doing here?'

'I need to talk to you. It's got worse. Worse since that night you ran down the stairs after me. You talked sense about Anna then, but now I've hit rock bottom. I've been caught on camera with Suzie.'

'Who's Suzie?'

'She's just a girl.'

'Mikey, nobody's just a girl. Get in the car. You're a sad lad. What am I going to do with you? Get in.'

Of all my brother's mates, Rob had always taken an interest

in me. Now I wanted to talk to him. 'Rob, I went round Megan's flat Saturday afternoon to see you on the off-chance, but you weren't around.'

'I was refereeing, but Megan rang me to say that you were trying to find me and that there'd been some drama, but she wouldn't say what happened.'

'Just as well, 'cos I crashed and burned, and it wasn't pretty. Kate Adams was there, and then Anna turned up, out of the blue.'

'Well, that's tough, Mikey, but you've got to face her sometime.'

'No, that's not it. Kate got out this photo of me snogging Suzie right in front of Anna. Talk about being shot down in a ball of flames! Suzie and I had got drunk at a party, and we ended up alone in the toilet. I was going out with Anna at the time, and seeing as Suzie is Anna's friend, afterwards we just agreed to forget about it and deny it if anyone rumbled us. But I don't understand how there can be a photo. The door was closed. OK, we were drunk, but . . .'

'Mikey, I'm going to struggle to come over all sympathetic here, pal.'

'I'm not asking for sympathy, Rob. I just want your opinion. Don't you think it's just too weird that this happened right after Dan threatened me with the idea of me and Michelle Saunders being caught in the act? Don't you think that's a bizarre coincidence? Maybe God is on my case after all, and he's, like, actually . . . you know . . . doing things. But I'm still officially an atheist, remember. And that's what you were. So can we talk about it, because I'm feeling so guilty, apart from anything else? How can I stop feeling so pants all the time?'

Rob needed to drive over to pick some gear up from Megan's flat. They were engaged, but they didn't live together – something you'd never have believed if you'd known Rob when he was my age. And that was the interest for me. Here was another normal person like me, like Dan, who'd been transformed by Christianity.

We ended up at one of my brother's old haunts. It was a sports social club on the edge of the estate where we used to live. It had a bar, and I'd had my first ever drink there. Rob and I were sitting in front of the TV in the corner. It was the news.

'I'll tell you now, Rob, that even if I was totally convinced by all the evidence for God, and even if Jesus turned up at my house, I'd still never want to be religious, because of this.'

Rob had no idea what I was talking about. 'Because of what?'

'Because of all the problems religion causes in the world. Do you realise that since we sat down here, in just two minutes of TV, we've had headlines about the hunt for Muslim fundamentalist terror networks, then Palestinians and Jews blowing each other up in Israel, then Catholics and Protestants killing each other in Northern Ireland? And what motivates these people to kill? Religion. What turns people into suicide bombers? Religion. Which makes me want to keep well out of it. Look at all the wars religion causes.'

'You're right,' Rob said, holding his hand up as if admitting a foul. 'There's been a catalogue of crimes committed in the name of Christianity from the Crusades right up until now.'

'And don't you think that turns people off?' I said. 'That's why people today still relate to that John Lennon song, "Imagine there's no heaven, it's easy if you try. No hell below us, above us only sky. Imagine all the people, living for today." I reckon John Lennon was right. If we could get rid of religion, we'd be giving ourselves half a chance. So I'm not too likely to sign up.'

Rob was staring at the screen as we watched another bomb go off somewhere in the Middle East. Then the report cut to a woman crying over a coffin – really wailing like you've never seen tears before.

'Look, Mikey,' Rob said, 'I feel as angry as you do watching this, but you've got to bear in mind that Jesus commands his followers to love their enemies, let alone their neighbours. Jesus is totally opposed to all this killing and carnage.'

'So why is it, in a place like Northern Ireland, where there are so many Christians and so many churches, that they've spent most of the last 30 years bombing each other?'

'Just because a terrorist says he's going to kill people in the name of Christ doesn't mean Christ has got anything to do with it. How would you like it if I set off a bomb and then claimed I did it in the name of Mikey Walters?'

'But it would be obvious I didn't do it.'

'Not if people failed to take the trouble to look into it. You could easily end up with a bad reputation, if no one checked the facts. And anyone who checks the facts will discover that sectarian violence in Northern Ireland has got nothing to do with real Christianity. Besides, the New Testament denounces violence. When you read it, you find that Jesus goes ballistic against hypocrites who claim to be doing God's will but actually do evil. Jesus despised that sort of man-made religion.'

'OK, then what about Muslims? They believe they're doing God's will just as much as you do, Rob!'

'Well, to be fair you need to talk to them, because I'm going to find it harder to defend Islam. In the Qur'an, Muslims are actually instructed to "fight and slay the pagans wherever you find them",[37] which seems to me to be a tough one to explain away, especially as the way Islam spread under Mohammed was through "holy wars" and bloodshed.'

'Exactly,' I said, 'and still today people detonate themselves because they've been promised heaven, which shows that the whole idea of religion is dangerous. Which is why I'm tempted to forget about the whole thing and stick with atheism. And if everyone else did the same, I reckon the world would be a much safer place.'

Rob's eyes widened as if I'd just blasphemed. It was the first time I'd ever seen him anything close to angry. 'Mikey, I'm afraid history proves the opposite. Atheistic governments killed more people in the last century than anyone else. A terrorist murdering in the name of Christ is distorting Christianity, but Hitler, Stalin, Mussolini and Chairman Mao were all being faithful to atheism when they killed millions.'

'Faithful?'

'Yes, utterly faithful and consistent. Think about Hitler. There he was, as a young man, reading Nietzsche's books, which said that God didn't exist. He drank it all in. He believed it. Nietzsche[38] was the first guy to be honest enough to say that if God doesn't exist, then there's no point behaving as if he does any longer. You might as well do what you want, and let evolution have its way, and let might be right. And where did that lead us?'

Rob flipped open his wallet and after going through cards and receipts, he found a battered scrap of paper, which he'd written on in biro. He plonked it in front of me, obviously wanting me to read it. It said: 'I freed Germany from the stupid and degrading fallacies of conscience and morality . . . we will train young people before whom the world will tremble. I want young people capable of violence – imperious, relentless and cruel.'

'Flippin' heck, Rob! What sort of a person carries a quote by Hitler around with them in their wallet?'

'I copied this down in Poland three years ago. I was backpacking, going round something called the Auschwitz visitor centre. I saw pictures of abused and castrated children. I saw Jewish hair made into cushions, and human fat made into soap. And to think that the Nazis emerged from the most educated nation in the history of mankind. And then in the

114

final room of the tour, this quote from Hitler is on a plaque hanging on the wall. I wrote it down because I was an atheist at the time, and I believed that conscience and morality were fallacies; that they were just human inventions which had no real authority. There was no God behind them. And it frightened the life out of me when I realised that Hitler had simply followed my views through to a logical conclusion.'

I was totally taken aback by Rob's sudden intensity. I'd unexpectedly tapped into something that had clearly set him on the road to converting to Christianity.

'Joseph Stalin and Chairman Mao were two of the biggest butchers in history,' Rob continued, 'and they were quite honest in saying that their atheism gave them licence to kill their own people. There was no higher power to restrain them. They couldn't see anything wrong with genocide if it served their political purposes.'

I was shocked into saying, 'OK Rob, perhaps giving atheism free rein isn't such a clever idea after all, but I'm not too impressed by the history of the church either.'

'Neither am I. And Mikey, abuses of power in church history are the worst possible advert for Jesus, and I'm hugely embarrassed by them, but you've got to remember that Jesus didn't tell his followers to set up any government. He never even tried to get political power. People wanted to make him King, but he would have none of it. He didn't believe in imposing his views by force. He wanted to get inside people's hearts. And there are signs in the church today of what Jesus is really like. Because for every crime committed in the name of Christ, I'll show you a hundred orphanages, hospitals, schools and soup kitchens started by Christians every day around the world.'

It wasn't so much that I found Rob's arguments persuasive, because I'm not sure I did. What impressed me was that he'd thought it all through – it wasn't blind faith. I'd thought nothing through. I just went with the flow. I'd had my fun with Michelle and Suzie, and I'd ended up feeling like a teenage dirtbag. I missed Anna every day, and because I'd trashed her, I'd lost a lot of my self-respect. I was even starting to lose my confidence.

So I'm unhappy. So what? So are most people, I guess. I'm still not convinced I should sign my life away and join the God Squad.

chapter 19

'Danny Boy, I just don't buy it,' Pete turned to me and said as we stood leaning against the wall of the cafeteria. The lunch queue wasn't moving. We were looking out on a sea of faces. There was a drone of conversation, and then a massive cheer as a plate was smashed somewhere at the back.

Andy asked, 'You don't buy what?'

'What Dan's just been telling us – that verse you quoted from the Bible. What was it again?'

'"I am the way and the truth and the life. No, one comes to the Father except through me." That's what Jesus said.'[39]

'Nice attitude!' Pete sneered, like a rapper posing for an album cover. 'I think you need to loosen up a bit and get with the twenty-first century. I mean, look in the far corner: you've got about 15 kids right there who are Muslims . . . and then there's Ranjit's crew over here, who are . . .'

'Hindus,' I helped him along, because he was building up to a question I'd been asking myself.

'And then there's this lot in front with the funny . . . what's it called?'

'Sikhs,' Andy said.

'And then there's about 300 of the rest of us in this hall right now who are . . . you know . . . mainstream, and I bet virtually all of us would say that it doesn't really matter what you believe, as long as you're sincere.'

Andy was murmuring in agreement: 'Are you saying, Dan, that you're right and everyone else is wrong? I mean, I've been your biggest supporter up till now, though perhaps I've not said as much, but I do agree with Pete on this one. Isn't it incredibly arrogant of you to say that you've cornered the market on truth?'

'Easy, tiger,' I said, trying to diffuse the situation. 'Any Christian will happily agree that there is truth in other religions.'

'Really?' Andy asked.

'Sure, I mean God's revealed himself in nature for a start. So someone can look at the mountains, oceans, deserts, stars and sky, and arrive at the idea of a "higher power". And wherever you go in the world people have a conscience. Virtually all societies that have ever existed have agreed on a similar set of things being right and wrong. And that gets you most of the way to the "golden rule", which is always to treat others the way you'd like them to treat you. And then many of us find out eventually that materialism doesn't satisfy. So there's a longing for something more. God's put eternity in our hearts, which is one of the reasons why there are so few atheists in the world. With all that to work with, I'd expect to find different religions springing up around the globe.'

'Exactly,' Andy said. 'So all religions are basically saying the same thing.'

'Andy, have you ever sat down with a Muslim and a Hindu and told them that they're both basically saying the same thing?'

'No,' Andy snapped, 'but that's what's so tragic. The way

117

people major on minor differences. You call him "God" and Islam calls him "Allah". So what? Why split hairs?'

'Well, if the only difference between Christianity and Islam was terminology,' I said, 'I'd agree with you, but there's just a bit more to it than that.'

'Like what?'

'Well, just about the whole shooting match. When we've got our lunch, why don't we sit with Ahmed and Shoaib on that table over there, and ask them?'

I'd been talking to some Muslim guys the week before about their faith. In fact I'd done the same with Hindus and Sikhs in my year at school. I'd even found a Bhuddist English teacher in one of the breaks. Remember, I didn't have exams to work for, and my coursework from the year before still counted.

Meanwhile, the queue still wasn't moving. Andy and Pete were getting frustrated. 'So why can't Islam and Christianity both be true?' Pete asked.

'Because Jesus either died on the cross or he didn't. The Bible says he did; the Qur'an says he didn't.[40] That's not a minor difference; that's the whole shebang. Jesus dying on the cross is the hardcore of Christianity. But if the Qur'an is correct and Jesus didn't die on the cross, then the whole of Christianity collapses. Guys, the whole message of the Bible is that sin is a problem that separates everyone from God, but Jesus' death on the cross solves the problem of sin for every-one who believes in him. Can I just explain exactly why Christians believe Jesus is the only way, and why only his death can solve the problem of sin?'

'No, let's just skip that,' Andy said. 'Keep going.'

'OK, well for reasons we can get into some other time, the Bible says that the only way to God is through Jesus' death on the cross. But if the Qur'an is correct in saying that Jesus never died on the cross, that bulldozes the foundation of Christianity. The whole thing comes crashing down and there's nothing left. You've destroyed Christianity totally.

'But if the Bible is accurate in saying that Jesus died on the cross and rose again, proving that he's God's Son, then Islam totally collapses. Because first of all God had a Son, which is an outrageous blasphemy to any Muslim.[41] It also means Allah deserted one of his prophets, Jesus, letting him die a shameful death on the cross, which they can't accept. And it means the Qur'an has got a huge mistake in it. That might not be a problem for you and me, but to a Muslim it's unthinkable. The big deal in Islam is the belief that every single word of the Qur'an was literally downloaded from God to Mohammed in Saudi Arabia.[42] But if Jesus actually did die on the cross, like all the other historical sources say he did,[43] then the Qur'an is wrong. That's "game over" for Islam.

'Jesus either died on the cross or he didn't. It's common sense! He can't be on the cross all day getting tortured to death, and not be on the cross at the same time. The Qur'an and the Bible cannot be equally true. Both claim to be telling the historical truth about what happened at the crucial moment, but one of them has to be wrong.'

We'd reached the stack of trays at last. Andy was rummaging for a spoon. 'Well, we'll wait and see what your actual Muslims say about it.'

'But guys,' I said, 'the differences between major religions are endless. Hindus say there are 300,000 gods, Bhuddists say there's no god, many New Agers believe they are god. Muslims believe in one powerful but detached God. So when Jesus said, "I am the way and the truth and the life. No one comes to the Father except through me," he was deliberately ruling out other claims. Bhudda did the same when he abandoned Hinduism. Mohammed rejected the Hindu idea of many gods, to say that Islam was the only way. Everyone's making claims that rule out other people's claims. These religions exclude each other.'

At that moment, Michelle Saunders swept in through the doors and jumped the queue. She just assumed that people would let her in at the front. And of course they did. There was a slight hush as she passed us. She was revered as a real woman in a sea of girls. It was like having Britney Spears visit your school every day.

'If all religious views are basically the same,' I said, 'that means Michelle Saunders believes the same thing as our Bhuddist English teacher. He told me yesterday that the whole goal of Bhuddism for him was that he wanted to extinguish his own personality so that he became nothing more than a drop in the ocean of reality. I don't think Michelle's ambition is to extinguish her own personality. I think she wants to be the next Victoria Beckham.

'And Ranjit, who runs the Hindu Society, told me that when he dies, he'll be reincarnated as an insect if he doesn't play his cards right. But Shoaib says that no one will ever be reincarnated. He says that when we die everyone who's ever lived will be judged by Allah and will spend eternity either in paradise or in hell. So it seems to me that Ranjit and Shoaib are not basically believing the same thing.'

'OK,' Pete said, 'maybe not believing the same thing, but connected to different aspects of the same thing. The way I see it, it's like a story I heard somewhere about three blind men all touching different parts of an elephant. There's a Muslim holding onto a leg, who says, "It's a tree. And I won't tolerate anyone telling me different." Then there's a Hindu holding onto the elephant's trunk and he says, "No, you're wrong. It's nothing like a tree. It's a hose. I'm certain of it." And then the Christian, who's holding the tail, says, "No, you're both wrong. It's a rope." But the reality is, Dan, you've each got a unique insight. You've each got a piece of the same truth. You're just describing it in different ways. If only you could see the bigger picture.'

Andy agreed: 'And that's why it's so arrogant for any of you to say that one single religious view is right and all the others are wrong.'

'But that's exactly what you're doing,' I said.

'What?' Andy and Pete said together in unison.

'You're saying that everyone else is blind except you. You're saying, "It's not a rope or a hose or a tree. You're all wrong." You're saying that Muslims, Hindus and Christians are all mistaken. You've just invented a story about an elephant which says that you're right and everyone else is blind and wrong. Isn't that just as arrogant?'

Pete was shaking his head. 'No, we're not saying anyone's blind. Let me try and explain it to you another way. There's a huge mountain, and God is at the top of it. But the Muslim is making his way up one side, and as far as he can see, his is the only path up. He doesn't realise that five miles away, round the other side, there's a Hindu chiselling out several different paths to the top. And neither of them knows that behind the clouds on the steep side there's a Christian climbing up, and he reckons that there's no other way. So you're all climbing towards the same God, but the Christian's coming from the European side of the mountain, and the Muslim's coming from North Africa, and the Hindu from Asia. All these religions are paths from different cultures and civilisations to the same place.'

'And where are you on the mountain?' I asked.

'How do you mean?'

'How do you know that these religions are going up different sides of the same mountain? Where's Pete watching all this from?'

'Well, from the top.'

'But you just said that God is at the top.'

'OK, so maybe I'm in a helicopter hovering over the top.'

'Whooah! Now you're above God. Pete! What's it like up

121

there? Isn't your helicopter backfiring on you? You're saying that every world religion is culturally conditioned, but that Pete Sykes has done something no Muslim, Hindu or Christian has ever managed: you've risen above your own culture, and even above God, so that you can see all these poor travellers toiling away up the mountain in their narrow-minded way. You're saying you've got a true picture of what's really going on, but millions of ignorant Christians and Muslims haven't.'

'Dan, I'm sorry, but it's just plain obvious that all religions lead to God.'

'But Pete, you don't tell us how you know so much about God. Your religious claim is as exclusive as everyone else's. In fact, your religious claim rules out everyone else's, but you don't feel the need to reveal your sources. Come on, let us in on the secret! How did you find out the truth? Where's your information coming from? It sounds so open-minded and generous when you say that all religions lead to God, but you don't seem to notice that you've just said you're right and everyone else is wrong.'

We got our sausages, chips and beans, and sat down. It had taken so long that lunch break was nearly over. Almost everyone else had gone, including Shoaib and his posse. Andy said, 'We'll talk to them tomorrow because I think we're onto something.'

'Onto what?' Pete asked.

Andy answered, 'I think we're getting somewhere. I think I understand the point of all this now. It stands to reason that you've got to be on top of the mountain to see the whole picture. The only way I can see where all the paths on the mountain end up is by putting myself in the place of God. You're obviously not God, Pete, and neither am I. We're not even pretending to have had any revelation from God, but Mohammed and Jesus are. So, seeing as we've given Jesus so much air time, shouldn't we give Mohammed a chance? What have we got to lose? Let's look into Islam. Come on, Pete. What d'you reckon?'

'I reckon you're on drugs, mate. I warned you about those pills, but you wouldn't listen. Andy, snap out of it. In your heart of hearts you're just like any other sane person in this world who believes that if there really is a just God, then the genuine followers of all religions will get to him in the end.'

Pete waved a sausage around on the end of his fork, without realising that it kind of detracted from the seriousness of his question: 'Danny Boy, surely a loving God would never reject people who had sincerely followed the religion they'd been brought up with?'

I paused because I'd been chewing on this one myself. Looking back to when I was talking science with Mikey, I always felt his objections were partly an excuse to carry on living the way he wanted to. On the other hand, Kate's questions about suffering were from the heart. They were gut-wrenchers that churned both of us up. And in the same way, I could see that Pete was genuinely troubled by an unnecessary fear that God would end up being unfair towards people.

'I reckon as long as you're sincere, that'll be good enough,' Pete said, still jabbing his sausage at me.

I eventually replied, 'Pete, that's a totally reasonable thing to say, and in some ways I'd like to agree with you, because it makes us and God look generous and tolerant. But when the stakes are so high, it's a bit worrying.'

'Why? What's worrying about it?'

'It's possible to be sincerely wrong. Pete, I'm worried that you see world religions as if they are nothing more than different flavours on an ice-cream stand. You think choosing between them is simply a matter of opinion. There are no dire consequences in choosing chocolate chip rather than strawberry. Nothing bad happens to you if you end up rejecting strawberry.

'But Christianity is more like gravity than an ice-cream preference. It's a fact rather than an opinion. You cannot escape the consequences of ignoring gravity. It's possible to sincerely believe that your parachute will open, but in a world where gravity exists, there are deadly consequences if you're sincerely wrong and it doesn't.

'And because all of us have sinned, we face deadly consequences. None of us is perfect enough for a perfect heaven. So the Bible says we end up going to an eternal death – a hell that is worse than anything you can possibly imagine, Pete. That's why we need to accept Jesus, the one person who will save us from the result of our sins.'

For the first time in our whole conversation, Pete looked uncomfortable. Not just with me, but with Andy too. Was something finally getting to him?

'I'm not that interested,' Pete said. 'I appreciate your sincerity, and that's why I struggle with you saying that other people's sincerity isn't enough.' He was staring straight down at his shoes while drumming with his knife and fork on the table. Then he said, 'To be honest, Dan, I don't think I want to take this any further. It's been fun these past two weeks, but unless you can persuade me to change my mind, I've had enough.'

'OK Pete, that's cool. Let me give it one last shot, then we'll quit. I think you're annoyed because you've been cornered into a choice you'd rather not have to make. You'd rather just forget all about it and wish it all away. It's like you've got two doctors giving you two different verdicts on your state of health. The first doctor says, "Pete, it's nothing to worry about. You've got a common cold. Go home – you'll be fine." But the other doctor says, "Oh no! I'm afraid I've got some bad news, Pete. You've got cancer and if it isn't treated, you're going to die. But we've caught it in time, and fortunately there's just one treatment that'll save you."

'In that situation, Pete, just because of the seriousness of what the second doctor's saying, I reckon you'd pursue it. His diagnosis is so drastic, you'd be a fool not to give higher priority to his claims. You wouldn't say to the second doctor, "Thanks Doc, but I'll take my chances. I'll be OK. Besides, I've heard about the treatment you recommend and I don't like the sound of it." You'd investigate the cancer diagnosis till the bitter end; till you were absolutely sure you'd got the all clear. And that's why you'd be a fool to reject Christianity without at least checking out its claims, when your whole eternal destiny is at stake if it turns out to be true.'

I'd got Pete's attention. At least he was now looking me in the eye.

'Pete, we'd never say that sincerity is all you need in medicine, in politics or even in a maths exam. It's possible to be sincerely wrong in going to war or in answering a question.'

He mumbled a 'yeah' in agreement, trying to look unflappable and cool, as if none of this touched him in any way.

'So how can you be so sure that sincerity is all you need when it comes to God? We need God to tell us what to believe about God.'

'Exactly,' Andy said. 'So it's only fair that we talk to the Muslims as well.'

The bell went right above our heads.

'Well, that'd be a great start,' I said. 'We'll do it tomorrow.'

'Whatever,' Pete sighed. 'But can I just put in a request that at some point I'm allowed to beat both of you up?'

We were late for class.

chapter 20

After school the following day we walked along the street with a mixture of excitement and nerves. None of us had ever been inside a mosque before. Suddenly, Pete stopped and cleared his throat as if he was about to deliver a speech.

'OK, I'm only prepared to go through with this if we establish some ground rules. First, I reserve the right to remain a normal person. Nothing anyone says about God or life or death is going to make the slightest difference to me. No one knows for sure about any of this stuff, and I'm perfectly happy as I am. Therefore nothing anyone can say means that I've got to change in any way. When I leave this . . . mosque . . . I'm going to carry on exactly as I am. There are questions, but no answers. There's no truth. It's all smoke and mirrors.' He stopped as suddenly as he'd started.

I said, 'Pete, I'm impressed. There were so many statements of faith in there, I think you deserve to win the school prize for religion. All you've got to do is live a perfect life, perform some major miracles, die and then rise from the dead, and you might even get some followers. Come on, let's go in.'

Shoaib and Ahmed had asked us to meet them at their mosque. Andy, Pete and I didn't really know what to expect. I'd got the English translation of the Qur'an out of the school library and read it through the night before. It's a lot shorter than you'd think. I'd underlined a few bits in pencil that I wanted to ask the guys about.

'Take your shoes off, man,' Shoaib said, grabbing Andy's arm.

We filed into a large empty room, which had a massive green carpet. Ahmed and Shoaib sat down on the floor in their socks, so we joined them. 'What's this all about?' Ahmed asked.

Andy said, 'Well, yesterday we asked Dan here whether he agreed that all religions were basically saying the same thing. He didn't agree, and says that you wouldn't agree either.'

Shoaib was extremely hard-working at school and streetwise outside it. He was something of a natural leader, and determined to become a professional cricketer. It was typically flamboyant of him to insist that we talk to him in a mosque. He adjusted his glasses to stare at Andy as if focusing on the question. 'Well, that depends. You're going to have to give me something more specific.'

'OK,' Andy said. 'Jesus is an important person in the Qur'an, right? Do you believe he's the Son of God?'

Ahmed flinched the moment Andy said it. 'That's blasphemy, man. That's the unforgivable sin.[44] You need to be careful.' They were both visibly offended. Andy had gone in on the worst possible opening question.

'How can God have a son?' Shoaib asked, shaking his head. 'That's disgusting!'

'Why's it disgusting?' Andy said, obviously shocked by the strength of feeling.

'Because you're saying Allah had sex with Mary. That makes Allah out to be nothing more than an animal.'

I tried to calm things down. 'Christians don't believe that God had sex with Mary. It might be easier to say that Jesus called God his Father.'

'How can Allah be a father? And if any father has a son, how can that be anything other than sexual?' Shoaib asked.

Pete had already decided that coming along was a big mistake. 'Time out, guys,' he said. 'Let's try something else.'

Andy said, 'OK. Dan told us that the Qur'an says that Jesus never died on the cross.'

'That's right,' Ahmed said. 'In fact, what's so sad is that Christians have actually twisted and corrupted their own Scriptures,[45] which is one of the reasons why Allah sent the Holy Qur'an as the last testament to set the record straight.'

I got out my English Qur'an. 'Here's the bit,' I said. 'I found it last night: "They claim, 'We killed Messiah Jesus, son of Mary, the Apostle of God.' But they killed him not, nor did they crucify him. They were under the illusion they had . . . Assuredly they did not kill him. On the contrary, God raised him to himself." '[46]

'That's what it means in English,' Shoaib said, 'but that's not the Holy Qur'an.'

'It isn't?' I asked.

'No, that's a translation, man. You can't translate a perfect book. You can only read the Qur'an in the original. What you just said is a good enough translation, but it's not the Qur'an.'

Pete looked bemused: 'Are you saying that if I wanted to read God's words, the only way I could possibly do it is by learning Arabic?'

'Of course, man,' Ahmed said. 'And ancient Arabic at that. Look, I know that sounds a bit weird to you, but the fact is that there's a Qur'an in heaven in Arabic and that's how it was dictated to the Prophet,[47] peace be upon him.'

'So God speaks Arabic?' Andy asked.

'Yep and the proof of it is that the Qur'an is a perfect book, with no contradictions and no errors, and when you know the Arabic, it has an almost hypnotic effect on you when you hear it being read out loud. It makes you feel all nice and relaxed.'

Andy and Pete looked at each other totally perplexed.

Shoaib was fully aware that we hadn't got off to a good start. He was searching for common ground: 'Look, let's just go back to Jesus for a second. The Qur'an says he's a very important prophet. Through Jesus, Allah healed the blind and cleansed lepers.[48] But we totally reject the idea that he was God's Son and that he died on the cross for the sins of the world. That bit is all made up by the Christians, who tried to turn one of Allah's prophets into something he was not.'

'So what happened on the day when everyone else thinks Jesus was crucified?' Andy asked.

'Judas got crucified instead of Jesus, or at least it was someone who looked like Jesus, and then the real Jesus ascended to heaven. In fact he's coming back one day, but when Jesus returns to earth it will be as a Muslim, and he'll burn every cross.'[49]

We were only three minutes into the discussion, but it was clear that we weren't all believing the same thing!

I wanted to throw in a question. 'Can anyone know for sure that their sins are forgiven?' I asked.

'No one knows for sure. We just wait and see if Allah wills it. Unless, of course, you die in a jihad. That's different. If you die in a holy war, you're guaranteed paradise.'

Andy said, 'But paradise isn't much fun for women, is it? Doesn't the Qur'an say that heaven is a lot of men being surrounded by beautiful virgins who wait on you hand and foot?'[50]

Shoaib said, 'People always bring that up. It's just picture language.'

'OK,' I said, 'what about this verse, which I found last night? Because this certainly isn't picture language. In this bit of the Qur'an, Muslims are commanded by God to "fight and slay the pagans wherever you find them"[51] and "fight those who believe not in Allah . . . until they pay the jizya with willing submission and feel themselves subdued".'[52]

'That's self-defence,' Ahmed said. 'Islam is a peace-loving religion.'

'Hang on a minute,' Pete said. 'Mohammed didn't spread

Islam by self-defence. He exported it by conquest, didn't he? And OK, I don't know much about the Bible or the Qur'an, but I can tell you one thing for sure: if you live in Saudi Arabia or Iran or Sudan, and you want to give up being a Muslim and believe in something else, you face the death penalty! That's not very peace-loving.'

'Look, you're confusing two different things, Pete,' Shoaib said. 'There's the Holy Qur'an and then there's Shariah law. Now actually, there's no country in the world where you've got full Shariah law. But I tell you what, if you had full Shariah law here, you'd certainly see an improvement!'

'What do you mean?'

'Well, for a start women wouldn't commit adultery because they'd run the risk of being stoned to death if they were caught, and thieves would stop stealing because they'd get their hands cut off. That'd do a lot more good than 80 hours' community service, or whatever punishment we have here.'

Pete was becoming involved emotionally in the discussion, which surprised all of us. He said, 'Now you're dodging the issue there, aren't you? There's no country in the world, where Christians are in the majority, where it's illegal to promote Islam, but there are lots of Muslim countries where you get arrested for promoting Christianity. That's not fair.'

Ahmed and Shoaib had a sort of 'Doh!' Homer Simpson reaction to this. They obviously felt they weren't getting anywhere with Pete. Ahmed said, 'Well, I'd agree with you if Islam was a false religion. But it's the true religion. There is no God except Allah, and Mohammed is his Prophet. So it's a good thing when a country becomes Muslim, and it's a bad thing whenever Islam is undermined.'

Shoaib could see that this had cut no ice with Pete and Andy. He said, 'Look, you can't just tear up someone else's culture. You can't just go to Saudi Arabia and say that women should have equal rights to men, and that converting to

Christianity is allowed. That's imposing your values on a foreign society. You've got to respect the right of any culture to protect what it deems sacred. You can't impose Western culture on places like Iran.'

Andy said, 'But aren't you being hypocritical? You'd like Britain to be a Muslim nation one day, right?'

'Yes, but I don't think that'll ever happen. Islam is an ideal that's never been fully tried yet,' Ahmed said.

'And Muslims campaign for equal rights here so that you can get your message across?'

'Of course, and it's outrageous how the media distort Islam so that people think we're all terrorist lunatics.'

Andy replied, 'So, if you campaign for freedom of speech here, why is freedom of speech and freedom of religion denied to Christians in Muslim nations? Aren't you guilty of double standards?'

Shoaib was becoming irritated. 'Guys, what's the point of this discussion?'

'To see if Christians and Muslims basically believe the same thing,' Andy replied.

'OK, let's try something else,' I said. 'Is Allah loving?'

Ahmed looked relieved to have a less inflammatory question to answer. 'Allah is merciful. Is that what you mean? What's behind the question?'

'Well, the Bible says that God is love, and that he's personal and can be personally known.'

Ahmed replied, 'No, Islam says that Allah cannot be known. Islam means submission. It's all about submitting yourself to Allah. It's more about respect than love.'[53]

I asked, 'So how do you get God's approval within your religion?'

'Well, you never know whether you've got his approval or not. But by living as a good Muslim, you give yourself the best possible chance. You've got the five pillars of Islam. Five things you need to do to get God's approval. One of them is coming here to pray, for instance. What do you have to do as a Christian to get God's approval?'

'I'm so glad you asked,' I replied. 'Nothing.'

'Nothing?'

'Yes, that's the glory of it all. Nothing. I don't claim to know much about other religions, but it seems to me that they all operate on a sort of points system similar to Islam. If you score enough points by obeying the rules, you earn God's approval. By contrast, Christianity says that no one can ever earn God's approval. There's nothing you can do to save yourself. Every religious scheme is woefully inadequate.'

'So you're totally stuck?' Shoaib asked.

'Exactly. It's like you're drowning in the sea,' I replied, 'and you've got all these instructions being shouted at you from different religious leaders standing on the cliff top. But it's confusing because they disagree on what would give you the best chance of saving yourself. Jesus is the only one who, rather than giving you orders, actually dives in to save you, losing his own life in the process. You do nothing, but God became a man and jumped into human history to save anyone willing to be saved by him.'

'What? How can God become a man? That's disgusting.'

'OK,' said Pete, standing up as if he'd heard enough, 'we're now going round in circles. And we're back where we started.'

'That's it?' Shoaib said, looking a bit disappointed. But Pete had obviously made up his mind he was leaving. 'Maybe next time I can tell you about the miracle of the Qur'an. Mohammed was illiterate, you know. Now how could an illiterate man have dictated the words of such a perfect book?'

Pete and Andy were walking towards the exit. 'I have absolutely no idea,' Pete said, 'but I think it's great that you've got your faith. Live and let live, that's what I say.'

I felt the need to apologise to Shoaib and Ahmed, because they'd hardly got a fair crack of the whip, but Pete had obviously run out of patience, and seeing as we'd worked so hard to get him along, we didn't really want to let him walk off on his own.

Outside in the street again, I wanted to close the deal. 'So what d'you reckon? It seems to me that to tell any Muslim to start believing that God had a son is pretty much asking them to stop being a Muslim. And to tell any Christian to go easy on the bit about Jesus being the Son of God is pretty much like asking them to stop being a Christian.'

We sat down at the bus stop, but it stank of urine. We sat on the wall instead. 'And it's very difficult to believe that Jesus was being crucified and not being crucified at the same time. It's tough to believe that I'm in England and in Los Angeles at the same time. How can Islam and Christianity be equally true?'

'I don't know,' Pete said.

'Pete, either Jesus died on the cross or he didn't. Islam and Christianity cannot both be true. History is terribly brutal to relativism.'

Pete said, 'I just don't want to become a narrow-minded bigot. I want to be as broad as possible.'

Andy replied, 'So do I, but I think if I was going to carry on saying that all religions are basically the same thing, or that all religions lead to God, I might as well also say that all flights from Heathrow go to Australia, or all roads from London go to Bristol. I'm sorry, Pete, but I think Dan's right. It boils down to a question of common sense.'

In saying that, I began to seriously wonder for the first time whether Andy was destined to become a Christian. He seemed to be following the evidence wherever it led, rather than sticking to his original opinion come what may. Then he added, 'All I'm saying is that this afternoon it's become obvious that all religions cannot be equally true. But even if I agreed that it's possible one of them might be true, how could I ever know which one?'

chapter 21

The doors swished open automatically and we were hit by a wall of sound. Hundreds of people erupted. Then beautiful music cut through the atmosphere. It was an enchanting melody, but with powerful bass underneath it. Still they cheered, and then within seconds the whole place was moving, bobbing up and down. When they got to the chorus, it felt like it was their theme song. Some of them were laughing. Church isn't like this, is it? But Dan tells me this is their regular Sunday evening church service. My name's Andy, and this is only the beginning. Later, I'm going to something called 'The Quest'.

Would I like to go to The Quest? It sounded like I'd need a virtual reality helmet, a laser gun or at least a Gamecube or Xbox. 'Oh no,' Dan said. 'It'll be like the chats we've been having – just with a few more people our age.' He'd reassured me that I wasn't going to have to sing anything or do anything weird. When I said I'd come, Dan must have thought that his luck was in. 'Hey, I can meet you at The Quest, or you could come along beforehand to church as well. It starts at 6.30 pm.' He'd promised me that The Quest was chilled out and that I'd love it. He'd given me no such guarantees about the evening service.

I'm fully aware of what I'm doing, by the way. By saying 'yes' to any of this, I'm crossing a line. A line which separates normal, happy, content people like me from organised religion, which is for people who feel the need for that sort of thing. I don't feel the need for any of it. But here I am all the same.

Where do these people get their energy from? I'd expected some middle-aged cheese, especially musically, but their 'worship' was phenomenal. If it had been simply a concert, I wouldn't have been too impressed, because the band weren't that good. If it had been simply a sing-song, I'd have had some sympathy for them, but there was another dimension happening, which I couldn't quite put my finger on.

They prayed spontaneously one after another, like surround sound popping up all over the auditorium. Then as a crescendo of singing rose and fell, a single voice burst through from the back. It sounded like Japanese. Dan whispered to me, 'This is cool. It's called a tongue.' I decided I was way out of my depth and sat down to just let it all sink in. I didn't really get the sermon. I was a bit distracted, looking around. I was asking myself, 'Are these people unusually ugly and strange?' Or, to put it another way, if I saw them all together down the shops, would I be able to tell they were Christians simply by the way they dressed? The horrible truth was, most of them looked like my parents. But that didn't explain why there were about 50 apparently normal teenagers sitting near us, with at least average good looks, who all seemed to be loving it.

Before The Quest began, Dan and I went outside to look for Kate and Anna, who'd agreed to join us. Supposedly Pete was coming too, but I was convinced he wouldn't show. Sure enough, the girls turned up but Pete didn't. He had his reputation to think about.

Upstairs, the room was draped in black, with one light trained on Dan's teacher friend, Rob, at the front. 'Welcome to The Quest,' Rob said.

I was shocked to see a couple of people there from school. There were about 30 of us in all, in table groups of five or six.

'Maybe you've come here tonight with a bellyful of second-hand opinions. Maybe a cynical teacher told you Christianity is just a legend that grew over time. With a TV documentary here, a throw-away comment down the pub there, and an avalanche of peer pressure, we get buried by the onslaught of busy lives. But in this room tonight, we'll fight our way up to the surface and begin The Quest.'

I turned to Dan. 'What the . . . ?'

'He's hamming it up,' Dan said. 'He always does this at the start of the evening, for newcomers. This is session five out of ten. Just hang in there.'

Rob continued: 'If you were selected for a jury, you'd have to swear an oath to put aside all preconceptions and give every bit of evidence a fair hearing. Our journey will take us beyond reasonable doubt. If you're ready, then let The Quest begin.'

Then there was a video presentation, which Rob introduced by saying: 'The only way you can get to know me, is if I come into your world and reveal myself to you. Observation and speculation will only get you so far. Until I really open up to you, you'll never know me. You need revelation. The same is true of God. We can spend a lifetime guessing, but unless God reveals himself, we're still in the dark. If a loving God exists, and made us to have a relationship with him, you'd expect him to communicate with us at some stage.

'All Christianity is saying is that God has done that through Jesus of Nazareth. God has revealed himself by coming into this world as a person. A person called Jesus. Tonight we'll ask whether that really happened. But at the end of The Quest is an experience. An experience that will enable you to touch eternal joy.'

The video presented a barrage of so-called evidence. At the

end of it, Rob joined us on our table. I waded straight in. 'Let's imagine I don't trust a single word in the Bible. Are there any mega-old non-Christian sources of information about Jesus?'

'Oh yes. Have a look,' Rob replied, opening up a course handbook. 'A Jewish first-century historian called Josephus says, "At this time there was a wise man who was called Jesus. His conduct was good and [he] was known to be virtuous. And many people from among the Jews and the other nations became his disciples. Pilate condemned him to be crucified and to die. But those who had become his disciples did not abandon his discipleship. They reported that he had appeared to them three days after his crucifixion, and that he was alive; accordingly he was perhaps the Messiah, concerning whom the prophets have recounted wonders." '[54]

'Flippin' heck!' Anna said. 'That's pretty much full-fat Christianity.'

'Yes,' Rob said, 'and what he says is backed up by the most important source we have: Tacitus. Tacitus was the main Roman historian of the period, and he confirms that Jesus was crucified "during the reign of Tiberius at the hands of one of our procurators, Pontius Pilate".'[55]

Rob went through several other references from people hostile to Christianity. In the handbook, he showed us quotes from Pliny the Younger,[56] Lucian[57] and the Jewish Talmud.[58]

'OK,' said Kate, 'I'm getting the picture. Can you just pull it all together? What does it all add up to? What would we know about Jesus from the ancient world if we totally ignored the Bible?'

'Well, you could be certain that Jesus existed, and you'd know quite a lot about him,' Rob said. 'First, both Josephus and Lucian say that Jesus was regarded as wise. Second, Pliny, the Talmud and Lucian imply he was a powerful and honoured teacher. Third, the Talmud indicates he performed miraculous feats, but was rejected by the Jewish leaders. Fourth, Tacitus, Josephus, the Talmud and Lucian all mention that he was crucified. Tacitus and Josephus say this happened under Pontius Pilate. And the Talmud says it was on the eve of Passover, exactly as the New Testament describes. Fifth, Josephus has reports of Jesus' resurrection, and sixth he says that Jesus' followers believed he was the Christ, or Messiah. And finally, both Pliny and Lucian indicate that Christians worshipped Jesus as God.'

This was a promising start. I hadn't expected there to be any unbiased support for the Bible's version of events. I thought Christians just believed it all with a massive leap of faith. But this just brought new questions into my mind. Kate then asked one of them: 'Haven't the stories in the Bible about Jesus got exaggerated over the years? I mean, they were written down a long time afterwards, weren't they?'

Rob was fairly laid back about it. He said, 'Well, by modern standards yes, but by ancient standards the New Testament is written so close to the events that it's like a newsflash.[59] The important thing is that much of the New Testament was written by eye-witnesses.[60] And if lots of eye-witnesses trooped into the witness box today and each independently described roughly the same sequence of events, that would be impressive evidence. More importantly, we know the New Testament books and letters were circulating at a time when there would also have been hostile eye-witnesses around who could have contradicted any exaggeration which had crept in. But they never did.'

I didn't like the sound of this. 'No, I reckon it's Chinese whispers,' I said, feeling a surge of confidence. 'The first person is told something like "Jesus is super and good" and tells a friend, who tells their friend, and by the time it's written down years later in the Bible it's been distorted into "Jesus is the Son of God", and hey presto, you've invented a new religion!'

Rob said, 'But when you play Chinese whispers, at the end of the game you get to hear what the original version was, because the person who started the whisper is still around to tell you how the whisper started off. And that's exactly the situation with the New Testament. Even if there was accidental or deliberate exaggeration going on in the years after Jesus' death, by and large the original eye-witnesses were the ones who wrote the New Testament. And they were in a better position than anyone else to write what really happened. Besides, when it comes to the resurrection of Jesus, we have got documentation that some scholars have dated to within a few months of the actual event.'[61]

Nervously I started to peel the plastic cup in front of me. I'd seen what a massive positive difference becoming a Christian had made to Dan, but I was still worried that for me to have the same experience, I'd have to believe a lot of crazy stuff. Like God landing on planet earth as an extraterrestrial carpenter. And I wasn't going to commit intellectual suicide, even if I was being promised the ride of my life in return. Besides, I knew what I was talking about.

'All this doesn't get you out of the woods,' I said, turning up the heat on Rob. 'Even if I accepted that the eye-witnesses didn't exaggerate, how do we know that we've got what they originally wrote?' I picked up Dan's Bible, which was lying on the table in front of us, and said, 'This is only a copy. And I know for a fact that the original documents are lost. So for all we know, during the copying process, all sorts of errors could have crept in. Someone told me that if the Bible writers were alive today, they wouldn't even recognise our Bible as what they originally wrote.'

'You're right that the original parchments have disappeared,' Rob said, 'but actually we do know for sure that we've got an accurate copy of the original, and here's why.' He turned to a table in the handbook[62] and spent about ten minutes explaining what it meant.[63] Then he summed it all up by saying: 'So, firstly we've seen that the oldest surviving fragment of the New Testament is a fragment of John's Gospel, which has been dated at AD 130. If we really wanted to, we could all jump in the car now and drive to Manchester, break into the John Rylands Library and see it. AD 130 is only 40 years after the original was written. To you and me that's a long time, but it's like a Xerox photocopy compared to other ancient texts, where the gap is anything up to 1,000 years. Yet even with a gap of 1,000 years, no scholar doubts the reliability of Tacitus or Livy, so the New Testament does very well by comparison.

'Secondly we've seen that where the New Testament really scores highly is in the vast number of manuscript copies we have. Because if you have stacks of ancient copies found all over the world and you put them all next to each other and find they're all essentially the same, then there can't have been exaggeration going on, otherwise they'd all be saying different things. If all the different copies are saying the same thing, then whoever's been doing the copying must have been copying very accurately. And, for the New Testament, there are over 5,000 Greek manuscripts, over 10,000 Latin manuscripts and 9,300 other manuscripts.'

Picking up the Bible for dramatic effect, Rob said, 'With so many early copies from so many places, all saying the same thing, we can be certain that the New Testament we have in our hands today is an accurate record of what was originally written.'

We'd reached the end of the evening. We got up from the table and wandered outside across the road to the chip shop. Rob's presentation had been impressive, but we all knew how much was at stake. Dan was buzzing, laughing and joking with the lads behind the counter. Kate and Anna were talking excitedly about whether they'd come back next week.

Fish 'n' chipped up, we wandered back into the street and started fighting over ketchup sachets. It was a clear night sky. I looked up at the stars and the moon. I guess I'd always suspected that some force or higher power made them. Now I was being told that their Creator loved me and that I could historically test whether he'd come into our world to prove it. Dan caught me in the act. 'When you've got enough evidence, Andy, get ready to invite God into your life,' he said, as if it was no big deal. 'And then you'll feel the difference.'

Maybe I was a step closer, but I comforted myself with the thought that I still had the freedom to walk away. I could forget all about God and carry on life as normal, if I wanted to.

chapter 22

It's Kate again. I'm walking along the street late at night on my own. Don't ask me why, or where I've been. I can't tell you. What I can tell you is that I think I'm being followed. I think there's a bloke about 100 metres behind me. When I turned into this street I saw him out of the corner of my eye. He's wearing a black leather jacket and a black woolly hat. There's no traffic, so I can hear his footsteps clearly . . . I'll cross the road for no reason, and if the footsteps cross as well, then I'm going to wet myself.

Here goes – I'm crossing the road now. Can I hear him cross too? . . . Yes. Oh no, what am I supposed to do? I'll get out my mobile. Where is the thing? . . . Typical! The battery's dead. This is a nightmare! I'll hold it up to my ear and pretend I'm on it and start talking loudly. I'm too scared to start running in case he chases me. I still want to believe I'll be OK.

And until he attacks me I am OK, aren't I?

I just want this to be over . . . I know what I'll do. That's it. I'll turn into this street I can see coming up here on the left. I'll walk straight up to the first house, put my finger on the doorbell, and if he walks straight on, I'll just watch him pass. But if he so much as looks like turning the corner after me, I'll ring the bell and scream so loudly the whole street will wake up.

This is it. I'm turning the corner. First terraced house in view. I'm opening a garden gate and going straight up to number 1. I've got my finger on the doorbell. He's turning! I'm pressing the bell. Nothing, no sound! It doesn't work! I am wetting myself.

I can see him. He's young.

'It's me . . . Nick.'

I nearly faint. It's Nick, my ex-boyfriend. Nightmare Nick, the scumbag from hell. I suppose I feel relieved, but I've never been so angry.

'What on earth do you think you're playing at? I could get you arrested for that. I'm serious. I could get you sent down, you little . . .'

'Chill out, babe. I'm only being friendly. I just wanted to see you – you know, properly – and you won't even talk to me.'

'Nick, what part of NO don't you understand?'

'Look, we had something special going on. You and me was cool. Why can't we just wipe the slate clean and start again? Come on, babe.'

'Listen Nick, I'm only going to say this once. First of all I'm not your babe. I'm not your anything and I never ever will be. And if you ever stalk me again like that, I'll go to the police and see that you're charged with rape.'

'What the . . . ?'

'You heard me, Nick. And you know exactly what I'm talking about. And if you so much as brush my arm in the lunch queue, or even try and talk to me again, I'll be down the police, filling out a form with a trained rape counsellor, and I'll go into a witness box and ruin your life. Do you understand?'

'But Kate, can't we even talk about it? I mean, even for old times' sake.'

'I'm warning you, Nick. Stay away from me, or I'll make it my mission in life to send you to prison.'

With that, I physically pushed him out of my way and ran all the way home. I didn't look back once. I slammed the door behind me and burst into tears.

chapter 23

Suzie here. In my opinion, every teenager should smoke pot – at least once, anyway. But being in this room again brings back a lot of bad memories of last summer, when it all got way out of control. This is Heather's house. Heather's parents are cool. In fact everything is cool as far as they're concerned, including drugs, believe it or not. I guess you don't know who Heather is. And I don't think you really know me either, do you? My name's Suzie, and I majorly fancy someone sitting across the room from me called Mikey. The problem is that he's a complete plonker, but I am too, so maybe we're made for each other. I've just lost one of my best mates, Anna, over him, which is stupid because we're not even going out. We're just two ships that pass in the night every now and again.

So you can't quite picture the scene, can you? Let me explain. It's 11.30 on a Saturday night, with the cast slumped around Heather's bedroom as follows.

On a beanbag to my left is Dan, who used to be a bit of a tart but is now suddenly different. Dan's stunned us all by getting himself 'born again' and all I can say is that he's now the most positive person I've ever met. For some reason to do with his new religious trip, he's quit smoking and he's 'not looking to go out with anyone at the moment'.

Then there's Andy. Andy is one of those annoying people who are impossibly clever but don't even try at school. He's quiet, but when he does say something it's usually worth waiting for.

There's hippy chick, Heather, who can wear clothes no one else could get away with. She's got her own personality going on, and it's all flowing flower power stuff. Like me, she's easy come, easy go.

Then there's the dark stallion in the corner. Pete, my soulmate, ex-boyfriend, sparring partner in crime, whatever. We've been buddies since primary school. We stopped going out when it felt like I was kissing my brother. Yuk!

And finally, there's Mikey, whose life bombed last month when in a totally uncharacteristic rash of honesty he spilt the beans about a fling with school witch Michelle Saunders. He lost his super-smart girlfriend Anna over it, and then got caught on camera with me, in a forgettable fumble in a toilet. Such is life.

As a group we've gone through phases. Last summer was a soft drugs and crazy stunts phase. But at the moment we're all deep and meaningful. No joking. When it's gone eleven at night we talk about God, garage and body piercing. Usually in that order.

'You see, I reckon you've changed,' Andy said to Pete, fishing for a response.

'How do you mean?'

144

'Last year, you would have slaughtered me if I'd gone to church. You would have thought it was hilarious. I'd never have heard the end of it. But I've just told you how much I enjoyed it and The Quest course, and you just shrug your shoulders and grunt.'

'Well, I guess.'

'You've softened, Pete. You're on the same slide as me. It's because you've realised that you're religious too. Dan's forced you to see that you're religious, even if you're atheist or agnostic. What you believe or don't believe about God is the basis for everything else in your life. Go on, admit it!'

'Well OK, if it's a crime, I plead guilty. I admit that I've probably just believed what most people my age in this country believe without ever really thinking about it.'

'You've accepted it all by faith,' Andy said, 'but you've never asked questions of your faith. And maybe we've all swallowed a lie. I mean, a week ago, for example, I would have said that the Bible was irrelevant to my life because everyone knows it can't be trusted. But going to The Quest has helped me see that it can be trusted.'

I was pretty sure Andy was missing the point. 'So what?' I said. 'Let's just say for the sake of argument that every single one of us here totally accepts the Bible as historical fact. That doesn't matter. What's important is that the Bible tells us there was this bloke called Jesus, who lived a good life, and he's a model we should all follow. And that if we were all like him, life would be beautiful. So Jesus is nothing more than a role model. I agree already. What's the big deal?'

Dan jumped in. 'The big deal is that if Jesus is nothing more than a role model, then he was the most successful liar in history.'

'You're just looking for a reaction, Dan,' I replied.

'OK, if I told you I was God, and promised you that it was within my power to guarantee you a place in heaven, I'd be lying. And if I got billions of followers, I'd be a successful liar.'

This was getting my brain in gear. I said, 'But what matters is that you believe he was God. Believing that Jesus is God helps you. Some people believe in yoga, some believe in yogurt. You believe Jesus was God and that inspires you. It's what you get out of your faith that matters.'

'But when all of us die, Suzie, we're all going to encounter ultimate reality. And if it's a carton of yogurt, I'll have lost nothing. But if it's Jesus Christ, sitting on a massive white throne of judgement, you'll have lost everything.'

'I'll take my chances,' I said.

There was a nervous silence from the others, which surprised me.

Dan asked, 'Suzie – who is Paul Drake?'

I replied, 'This is getting surreal. Why have the rest of you gone quiet? Who is Paul Drake? I've no idea. Is this a joke?'

'It doesn't matter who Paul Drake is because he's not claiming to be your God, your Creator, your Judge and your only chance of salvation. Paul Drake is a carpenter who's just made some fitted wardrobes for my mum. Unlike Paul Drake, Jesus of Nazareth is a carpenter making some bizarre claims. For example . . .'

'Oh, very clever,' I interrupted.

Mikey then surprised us all by saying, 'Clever – whatever. It's still the 64 million dollar question. I don't mind telling all of you now that I think I do believe in God. There you are, Dan, I've said it! And Dan, if you're saying that God's become a regular person – you know, a proper human being – and that this same Jewish first-century carpenter is going to judge me when I die, then you need to convince all of us.'

The tide was turning against me. First Andy and now Mikey were getting sucked into Dan's vortex. Still, it was more inter-esting than the usual rubbish we talked about. I gave in by saying, 'Fair enough. Hit me with your best shot. Who's going to start?'

Mikey continued: 'Andy is the cleverest out of us, and he's suddenly been convinced that the Bible can be trusted. So, just for tonight, let's say for the sake of argument that's a given. Go on, Dan, this is your chance. Tell us why you think Jesus is God.'

'OK, let's back up a bit. If I wanted to persuade you that Paul Drake is God, I'd first of all have to convince you that he even made such an outrageous claim. Only a tiny number of human beings have ever claimed to be God. Most were suffering mental illness and few won any followers, 'cos it's a pretty demanding role.

'But at Jesus' trial, the Jewish high priest asks him the question point blank and Jesus answers, "I am." Then it all kicks off. "Why do we need any more witnesses?" the high priest asks. "You have heard the blasphemy. What do you think?" And they all decide to kill him. Jesus tells them that one day he'll visibly return to earth in the clouds![64] I mean, come on! It's different biscuits from your average carpenter.'

This sparked Heather, who'd been deafeningly quiet, into action: 'I can't believe anything as freaky as that. I mean, Jesus' disciples may have swallowed this kind of stuff, but people were pretty ignorant and gullible back then. If I'd been there I would have been a lot more sceptical.'

Dan replied, 'Actually, the disciples were sceptical. Take Thomas, for example. The report's gone out that Jesus has risen from the dead, but Thomas won't believe a word of it. He says exactly what we'd have said if we'd been there: "Unless I put my finger into the nail holes in his hands, and unless I put my fist into the hole in his side where the spear was thrust through him, I won't believe it."

'And then there comes the heart-stopping moment when the resurrected Jesus turns up, and Jesus says, "Go on then, touch me." And when Thomas reaches out and discovers it's all for real, he says to Jesus, "My Lord and my God!" which is a cracking opportunity for Jesus to reply, "Oh no, Thomas. Get up off your knees, you dozy so and so. Stop worshipping me. I'm not God, I'm just a great moral teacher. I just say wise things and swan around being kind to people. I'm not God. Whatever gave you that idea? I'm just a role model." But Jesus doesn't say that. He tells Thomas off for being so slow to believe the truth!'[65]

'Crikey!' Andy said.

'Exactly. That's the power-play. It's Jesus who goes overboard making claims about himself. He doesn't talk up love, beauty or justice. He goes around saying that he's the answer to everything. He points to himself as the truth, as God on legs.'[66]

'That's pretty crude, isn't it?' Heather asked.

'Well, what else should we make of a man who went around "forgiving sins"? I mean, can you imagine how incredibly annoying that would be? I get knocked off my bike by a lorry, and Jesus is a pedestrian who comes up to us and says to the lorry driver: "I forgive you." I'd then say, "And who do you think you are? The Lord God Almighty?" I'd tell Jesus to mind his own business. What sort of a human being goes around forgiving sins?'[67]

'Then he predicts that he's going to be killed off, but he says, "Don't worry. Three days later I'm going to be raised from the dead,[68] and then I'll ascend to heaven." And then comes the bit where he really goes loony tunes. He says that at some point in the future he's going to appear in the sky and return visibly to the planet with all the angels. And then this carpenter from Nazareth will sit on his throne in heavenly glory. And everyone who's ever lived will be resurrected and gathered before him, and he'll judge them all. Some will go to heaven and enjoy eternal life; others will go away to eternal punishment. And get this: what's the basis for who goes where? Jesus says that it's how you respond to him in this life! Jesus claims he's not only the Judge, but also the basis for judgement.'[69]

Andy said, 'And so at this point I guess it does matter whether Jesus is telling the truth. Because if he is telling us the truth, we're going to meet him whether we believe in him or not! I don't know if I like the sound of that.'

'Exactly,' Dan replied. 'Paul Drake isn't claiming to be your judge beyond the grave. Jesus is. Which is why it matters who Jesus is.'

Well, that was logical, I had to agree. Of course I'd never studied the Bible, and I had thought it was all 'gentle Jesus, meek and mild'. I hadn't realised that Jesus said such extra-ordinary things. 'OK, I've got my facts wrong,' I said. 'But I still don't feel like putting Jesus at the top of my list of things to do.'

'Whoa, hold on just a minute,' Heather said. 'We've proved nothing yet. Jesus claimed to be God, but loads of people make stupid claims.'

'Precisely,' Mikey said. 'There must be hundreds of people in psychiatric care who will all swear blind that they're the president of the USA. But they're not.'

'Maybe Jesus was on speed,' Heather said. 'One time I was so stoned I thought I was in Destiny's Child. I thought I was Beyoncé, but I wasn't.'

Pete cut through the laughter. 'No, I reckon Jesus was some sort of crowd manipulator. He had the gift of the gab, so he shouted his mouth off and won a massive following.'

Dan replied, 'Well, he must have been pretty stupid too, 'cos he got himself killed in the process, and didn't make a single penny out of it.'

'But there are alternatives,' Andy said, 'aren't there?'

'Oh yeah. This is what we'll be doing tomorrow night at The Quest. It seems there are only three possibilities.

Someone once said Jesus was liar, lunatic or lord. The session's called 'Bad, Mad or God?' If he knew he wasn't God, then he was a liar. If he wasn't God but genuinely thought he was, then he was a lunatic.'

There was a pause at this point. I think because the epic scale of it all was sinking in.

Mikey broke the silence: 'So this is a smackdown either way, isn't it? If he's not God, then we've rumbled the biggest deception in the history of the world, but if he is God, well, that's a big deal too.'

'OK, so let's begin with the "liar, liar" thing,' Dan responded. 'Remember we're talking here about a horribly evil liar who sends people to their death by guaranteeing them heaven. Jesus encouraged his followers to be martyred if that's what it took, but if he knew he couldn't deliver paradise, that makes him a monster! And if he was a liar, then he really was taking the mick, because first of all he deceived the world into thinking he was the holiest man ever, and he taught people to live as pure as the driven snow. What's more, he really pushed the boat out when he claimed to be sinless. But Jesus-the-liar pulled it off. Surrounded by his bitterest enemies, he challenged them to name a single sin he'd committed, and none of them could.[70]

'If he's a liar, what are we supposed to make of his love for lepers, prostitutes and the poor? He spent most of his time with the outcasts of society. But the clincher for me is his avoidable death. He gets killed for claiming to be God, remember? What's to be gained by dying for something you know isn't true? Why go through with the pretence? And even when he's on the cross, when they're literally killing him and he's got only minutes left to live, what comes out of him? Pure love. He prays for his murderers: "Father, forgive them, they don't know what they're doing." '[71]

Andy said, 'Yes, I'd agree that at that point he's got nothing left to gain by carrying on the act. He looks genuine. Deluded perhaps, but genuine. Sorry, Pete, I don't think Jesus was deliberately lying.'

Pete huffed in his typical way. 'I'd agree that promising people heaven is pretty cruel when you know you're just an ordinary Joe who can't deliver. Heck, maybe he was deluded. Maybe he was nuts?'

'I love it,' I said. 'Was Jesus nuts? Discuss.'

'I think this is much more likely,' Mikey said. 'It's absurd to say that Jesus was a conman. But he might have been a lunatic. I mean, they weren't too clued up about personality disorders back then, you know.'

Dan said, 'You'd think this one would win some supporters, but no psychiatrist will sign up for it, because Jesus shows no signs of being mentally ill. Quite the opposite. You'd expect that anyone who was as egocentric and egotistic as Jesus – I mean constantly talking about himself as the answer to every-thing – anyone who spoke like that would come over as un-stable and unbearably arrogant. Yet there's no doubt Jesus was thought by everyone to be the most humble person imagin-able.

'Besides, are we really going to say that our entire legal system and the last 2,000 years of European history have all been founded on the sayings of a lunatic? No one's improved on Jesus' teaching. I dare anyone to read Jesus' famous Sermon on the Mount and then say he was a lunatic.[72] If Jesus was mad, then strike me down with insanity!

'And what are you going to do with the miracles? They're going to take a lot of explaining away. Remember, even Jesus' opponents agreed that he worked wonders.[73] They're even recorded outside the Bible.[74]

'And how about the prophecies? Jesus fulfilled 322 proph-ecies which were written down at least 400 years before his birth! Many of them are minutely specific things which he would have had no control over.[75] I suppose a lunatic could have got lucky and fulfilled a few prophecies, or a liar might have been able to arrange a few deliberately. But I challenge anyone to read all 322 Old Testament prophecies and say that any liar or lunatic could possibly have pulled off more than a handful. Yet Jesus fulfilled 29 of them on the day he died. So . . .'

'So,' Andy said, 'the options are narrowing, and it becomes a bit scary.'

Mikey added: 'To be fair to Dan, I'd have to admit that it's going to be a very bold shout to say Jesus was bad or mad, but it's still a tough call to say any human being was God.'

Dan replied, 'I agree, but when you've eliminated the only possible alternatives, there's nowhere else to turn. And besides, if God did come to earth as a man, you'd expect that man to be the most famous man who ever lived. You'd expect his birthday to split history in two. You'd expect his teaching, his miracles and his character to smash a hole in the history of the planet so big that billions of people would push their way through it to follow him. You'd expect a God-man to make the sort of impact that Jesus of Nazareth did.'

Pete said, 'Well, I still can't buy it.'

Dan replied, 'That's fine, because I'd take everything we've said tonight as no more than a back-up argument for Christianity being true.'

'You mean the whole evening's been a waste of time?'

'No, I think the great thing about tonight is that it just shows you that you can make a watertight case for Jesus being God, even without the strongest single piece of evidence.'

'You mean you've left something out? Well, what the hell is it?' Heather asked, standing up in frustration.

'The documented physical resurrection of Jesus of Nazareth. It's the rock against which every alternative theory smashes into pieces.'

Pete said, 'You're saying all that stuff tonight is only your back-up argument for Jesus being God?'

'Exactly.'

'You slag!' Pete said, launching himself across the room in what turned out to be a mass bundle. Everyone joined in. We had something of a tradition of throwing Dan's trousers out of the window, and seeing as we hadn't done it since his accident, we decided that this was the moment. Pete was particularly efficient at de-bagging his victims. Dan's jeans went sailing gloriously down into the street below.

In his boxer shorts, to our hoots of delight, Dan ran downstairs and out into the road, where he did a lap of honour, avoiding a couple of passing cars. And we weren't even drunk.

Heather's mum came in to see what all the noise was about.

'Jesus,' Andy replied.

chapter 24

Oh no! She's coming in my direction. We're in the science block entrance at the start of lunch break. I don't know if I can do this.

'Anna . . . look, I'm really sorry . . .' Suzie said. She paused, obviously waiting for me to tell her it was all OK, but seeing as it wasn't OK, I let her sweat. I'd been dreading this apology as much as I'd been looking forward to it. I did want to stay friends with Suzie, but she was going to have to grovel big time. I huffed and stared past her, with an expression which hopefully said 'I don't need Mikey and I don't need you'.

But the truth was, even though I'd been so hurt by what Suzie had done, I'd absolutely hated avoiding her in the corridors, seeing who would be the first to crack and break our stony silence. I was determined it should be her. Now I was going to enjoy her pain.

Suzie continued: 'You know, I really am sorry, and I know I need to apologise. I've been such a coward not saying anything till now. You're the last person I'd ever want to do this to.'

'So what exactly are you apologising for?' I said, forcing her to name her crime, to make it even more agonising for her.

'You know,' she said.

'No. Do spell it out for me,' I replied, 'because I'm a bit confused. You see, I had this friend called Suzie and I also had a boyfriend called Mikey, and there's this sort of unwritten rule that decent human beings generally sign up to, which is that you don't try and steal other people's boyfriends. Perhaps you've never come across it, but it's a sort of universal thing – you know . . .'

'Look, I can explain everything, Anna, because it's not actually what it seems.'

'Oh, let me guess,' I said. 'You bumped your head and in a sudden bout of amnesia, you forgot that you had a friend called Anna. Or maybe you forgot that Mikey was my boyfriend. Or maybe . . .'

'Anna, you've every right to be angry, and I don't have any excuse other than that we were both drunk at a party, and if it's any consolation or of any interest to you, we were only together for about five minutes, but obviously in that time someone took a photo. I still have no idea to this day who took it or how that happened, but it serves us both right that we got caught.'

I couldn't keep up the pretence of not being interested in renewing our friendship any longer. I did care about Suzie. I was just sure that if I said so I'd start to cry. Trying to hold it together I said, 'But Suze, why didn't you tell me? If you'd come up to me the next day and said, "I've done something horrible while I was drunk and I didn't want you to find out from anyone else. So here goes . . ." things might have been different. But you didn't. You said nothing. Why?'

Suzie replied, 'Because there's not anything going on between me and Mikey, and it's only ever happened once before – about a year ago, before you were even here at our school. And we both regretted it afterwards, and we were well out of order, OK? We didn't know that we were going to be photographed. We just agreed to forget all about it. It was all very embarrassing.'

'Fine,' I said as sarcastically as possible, flicking my hair as I snapped my head away from her to walk off. I felt good that my hair was so much better than hers. 'That's just great,' I said with some venom. 'Makes me feel a whole lot better.'

'Wait,' Suzie said, running after me. Maybe she was going to grovel after all. Result! 'There's something else. This isn't just an apology – it's also an offer.'

'An offer of what?'

'A holiday.'

I was astonished by her stupidity. I said, 'Let's just get this straight. You're offering me a holiday to try and make up for the fact that you got caught kissing my boyfriend in a toilet?'

'No, it's not like that – honestly it isn't. The fact is, we're all going. Or at least we're all hoping to go. We started planning without you. It's during the summer holidays and I said to everyone that we would have made up by then, so I just want you to come. Please, please come, Anna. It's the most amazing opportunity. A once in a lifetime . . .'

'Suzie, what on earth are you talking about?'

'Malaysia,' she said.

'What? How are you going to afford to go to Malaysia?'

'That's the beauty of it. We don't have to pay. Well, we've only got to pay a part of it. We've each got to raise only £500.'

'But it's the other side of the world. The flight alone's got to be more than £500.'

Suzie then explained that her brother had a friend at university who was organising a scuba-diving trip to Malaysia. He'd got some money from a grant-making body and some sort of corporate sponsorship to work for the Malaysian Department of the Environment. I didn't really understand it. We were supposed to survey fish living near a remote coral reef. But how could we possibly do that? Suzie seemed convinced that we could all take a beginner's diving course and then fly to Malaysia to do research for the real scientists. She went on and on about the problems of over-fishing in Malaysia, and how we'd end up saving some species from extinction and we'd be castaway in paradise. It sounded totally unrealistic. What was important was that we were talking again, and it was a relief more than anything else.

As we slammed our lockers and said goodbye, she asked quite unexpectedly: 'What are you doing Sunday night?'

It was an awkward question, because I was planning to go back to Dan's evening Quest series, but I didn't want to admit it. I didn't want Suzie to think I'd gone soft. 'Dunno,' I said.

'Only I'd quite like to go to the God course thing, and Dan said that you and Andy were going, so I wondered whether now we're talking again I could come along?'

chapter 25

Pete here. You've not heard from me directly till now, but I guess you're aware that the others are showing signs of giving in. Mikey now seems to think that science proves God or something, whereas I'd always thought the opposite was the case. He also thinks God's 'got his number', whatever that means. Andy doesn't have much of a life anyway, so he's vulnerable to this sort of thing. Anna sees God as the answer to her relationship turmoil, and even me old mucker Suzie is sniffing around the subject. As for me, I'm gloriously detached from it all. I just think all this is part of growing up. You know, talking about the meaning of life and stuff. After Dan first told us about his weird experiences, I expected to lose interest. But I'm not ashamed to say that I have started to wonder whether life does have some greater purpose. And seeing as everyone (except Mikey) is going, I've finally agreed to go to The Quest, which the others promise is right up my street.

Well, here we are outside Dan's church. The breaking news is that Suzie and Anna have officially made up, which means the only remaining people that aren't talking to each other are Anna and Mikey. We've signed them both up for the summer scuba madness in Malaysia, but not told them yet, so they're going to have to bury the hatchet eventually. For the time being, because Anna's here, Mikey isn't, which is a shame because all the rest of them seem to think that going along to Dan's church service beforehand is a great idea. If Mikey were with me, I'd have an excuse to go off with him and do something else. As it is, I'm being roped in.

Two hours later

Well, that was just about the most disturbing experience of my life. Either those people are seriously deluded, or I don't know what. Someone needs to psychoanalyse them. They hear voices, you know. It's all 'God's told me this' and 'God's saying that'. They also speak in different languages that they

157

don't understand, which is impressive when you hear it. The atmosphere in there is awesome. I mean, there's definitely something going on. I've never been in a church like that before. And although most of it made me want to run a mile, I also felt as if I wanted to cry on at least two occasions. Which probably just shows that there's a lot of emotions running high in there. Dan thinks it's 'the Holy Spirit', but that's the sort of cheese that makes me want to barf. Anyway, I feel a lot more comfortable up here, sitting round a table.

'Welcome to The Quest,' a guy in his early 20s said from the front. Apparently he's a friend of Mikey's brother.

Clicking PowerPoint slides up on the screen, he said, 'We saw last week why the popular view that Jesus was no more than a great moral teacher doesn't fit the facts. We saw that Jesus' claims to be God were so outrageous and extreme that the only alternatives open to us are to say (1) that Jesus was an evil man who deliberately set out to deceive people into thinking he was the unique Son of God, when he knew he wasn't, or (2) that Jesus was insane in that he was convinced he was the unique Son of God, when actually he wasn't, or (3) that his claims were true. And we asked, "Which of the three possible verdicts best fits the facts?" Tonight we look at one final piece of evidence: his resurrection from the dead.'

A video started. We were sitting right at the back. I turned to Dan and whispered, 'So what? Even if he does convince us that Jesus rose from the dead, so what? How can anything that happened so long ago make any difference to me? It's irrelevant. I'm going to do whatever I want, no matter what evidence he comes up with, and so will everyone else.'

Dan replied, 'But what if I introduced you to that carpenter I told you about who's doing some work for my mum, Paul Drake, and Paul Drake says, "They're going to kill me, Pete, but after they've buried me, three days later I'll rise from the dead, and then we'll go out for a meal to celebrate. And my resurrection will be the proof that I'm the Son of God and the key to your eternal destiny"?'

'I'd either ignore him or call social services,' I said.

'Exactly. But what if you next saw him on the six o'clock news murdered, certified dead on arrival at hospital and then buried. And then three days later, he comes up to you in Burger King and says "Hi"?'

'Well, he'd certainly have done a great job of getting my attention.'

'You'd take his claim to be God and the key to your eternal destiny a little more seriously, wouldn't you?'

'Yes, but generally speaking dead people stay dead.'

'But Pete, if it's even possible that God exists and that miracles can happen, then it's at least possible that Jesus rose from the dead. One miracle is as easy to believe as another.'

'But I'm happy as I am,' I said.

'But Pete, God's the greatest pleasure in life.' Dan sipped his drink while he thought for a moment. 'The trouble with you is that you're not committed enough to enjoying yourself.'

'What?' I said, taken aback by an unexpected slur on my reputation as a major league party animal.

'You're far too easily pleased, Pete. If you were really serious about enjoying life, you'd become a Christian. I've been on your side of the fence and done all the stuff you've done, and I can tell you that a relationship with God is much more exciting. It's the utter business, and it's only possible through faith in Christ's death and resurrection.'

What annoyed me about Dan was that he did seem to get more out of life than we did, though I still couldn't see how I could ever change as much as he had.

'There are more than a billion Christians alive today,' the video soundtrack boomed, 'and they'd say the evidence for the resurrection proves that God's not all in the mind. The resurrection evidence shows that Christianity is true – not just for me, but for everyone. Because I can be sure Jesus rose from the dead, I know that Jesus has proved his claims to be true; that he's alive today. So through faith in him and his resurrection, I know that I can enjoy a relationship with God right now that totally satisfies me and which will go on for ever.'

We broke into small group discussion. Rob was our 'table leader', which sounded pathetic. As soon as he sat down, I went on the attack: 'It's all guesswork, isn't it? Nobody really knows what happened.'

Andy joined in. 'Do we know anything for sure?' he asked. 'Is there any single fact about the resurrection which is uncontested?'

'Yes,' Rob said. 'For starters, the fact that the tomb was empty. It is an undisputed fact that Jesus' dead body disappeared. Even an atheist historian will tell you that on the third day the tomb was empty. Three days after Jesus' body was buried, it simply wasn't there.'

'How do you know that?' Kate asked.

'Because all historians agree that if Jesus' dead body had been in the tomb, then the Jews or Romans would have produced it as soon as the first Christians started claiming that Jesus was alive. Remember, Jesus of Nazareth had been such a blasphemous threat to the Jews and such a political threat to the Romans that they conspired together to crucify him. The whole point was to snuff out Jesus and his movement. So the last thing they wanted was Jesus' disciples persuading people he'd risen from the dead. If they'd had the body, then as the disciples toured Jerusalem saying, "Christ is risen," the Jews or Romans would have put Jesus' corpse on a cart and wheeled him round Jerusalem saying, "No he's not. Come and see for yourselves. Here's his dead body." Jesus was a celebrity, remember.

'You see, strictly speaking, Christianity should not exist. It should never have got off the ground. The so-called "resurrection appearances" should have been instantly disproved by both the Romans and the Jews, who had the dead body of Jesus in a sealed tomb, guarded by soldiers. But neither the Jews nor the Romans ever did produce the body. That's because they themselves could see that the tomb was empty.

'Even an atheist historian will tell you that the Jews and Romans would have produced the body if they'd had it. The reason they didn't was because Jesus had gone missing. The best they could do to explain the empty tomb was to make up a pretty unconvincing story that Jesus' disciples had stolen his body while all the guards had fallen asleep,[76] which, if nothing else, proves that they didn't have the body.'

Suzie then said, 'OK, but I think I've thought of an alternative explanation. I know this will sound a bit far-fetched but, quite honestly, so does the resurrection idea. So here goes . . . what if they took Jesus down from the cross too early? I mean before he was actually dead? He then recovers in the tomb, and then when he meets the disciples they all think he's resurrected!'

Rob said, 'Nice one. What do you guys reckon?'

Dan said, 'If so, you've got to admire his stamina, because first of all he was whipped 39 times before he even got to the cross. The course book says that sometimes people sentenced to crucifixion never even made it to the cross; they died during the flogging.'

Dan began to describe a Roman flogging in an alarming degree of detail.[77] Christians obviously take a perverse pleasure in talking about their hero's ordeal.

'And the chances are,' Andy said, 'that the Romans didn't muck about. I guess they were experts at executing people.'

'These soldiers were a professional crucifixion team,' Rob said. 'It was their job. Besides, if a prisoner escaped death, the responsible soldiers would be put to death themselves! So they had a huge incentive to make absolutely sure that Jesus was dead before they removed his body from the cross.'

'Anyway,' Anna chipped in, 'didn't they thrust a spear into his heart to finish him off?'

'Actually,' Megan (who I'd not met before) said, 'we now know that the separated water and blood which flowed out of the spear wound is good medical evidence that Jesus was already dead.'[78]

Kate said, 'I'm sorry, guys, but I can't believe we're even discussing this. Of course he was dead. And even if he wasn't, how would he be strong enough to roll away the stone and fight off all the guards?'

'So,' Rob said, 'the idea that Jesus never died on the cross asks us to believe that a man could survive a Roman flogging, a crucifixion and a spear through his heart, and then unwrap himself from yards of cloth probably soaked in 34 kilograms of spice, push away a huge stone, fight his way past up to 16 guards, and then appear to his disciples as the picture of health, convincing them that one day they could have a glorious resurrection body like his. More importantly, this explanation also requires Jesus to become a liar and a hoaxer, who contrived the world's most elaborate deception: Christianity. This is contrary to everything else we know about him.'

'OK, the poor bloke was dead,' I said, 'but I've also got another possibility . . . suppose the tomb was empty because Jesus' disciples had stolen his body!'

'Tomb raiders!' Andy cried out mockingly, mimicking an action sequence that prompted the others to take up various martial arts poses. The shouts of 'Hah!' caused people on the next table to look over, wondering why we were practising kung-fu kicks.

'No listen,' I said. 'Most likely they were gutted that Jesus had died and they probably sat around wondering what to do next. Maybe they hit on the idea of turning a negative into a positive. So they stole the body and then claimed they'd seen Jesus . . . I dunno . . . having a coffee at Starbucks . . . to keep the dream alive.'

No one seemed very impressed with my suggestion, but at least I was thinking creatively, rather than just swallowing it all like the others seemed to be doing.

Megan replied, 'Let's imagine that the disciples did steal the body. I find that hard to believe, to start with because these men were strict Jews, who lived to a very high moral standard. They were very scrupulous when it came to matters of the conscience. But are we really going to say that these people went all over the world telling people Jesus had risen from the dead when they knew it was really only a miserable lie? When they knew in their hearts that Jesus wasn't risen at all, and they'd just nicked the body and buried it somewhere?'

'Stranger things have happened,' I said.

'Pete, the biggest problem with your argument,' Dan said, 'is that the disciples didn't just say that Jesus was risen; they actually died for it.'

'That's not a problem at all,' I replied. 'Loads of people die for their religious beliefs.'

'Precisely,' Rob said. 'People die for what they believe in. Nobody dies for something they know isn't true. The disciples were in the unique position of knowing without a doubt whether or not they were tomb raiders. If they'd stolen the body and somehow hoaxed the resurrection appearances, they wouldn't have allowed themselves to be tortured to death for it.

'You see, the disciples were literally crucified for their belief in the resurrection. Right up until the last minute they could have escaped death simply by admitting that they'd stolen Jesus' body. If the resurrection was a scam they'd invented, don't you think at least one of them would have cracked and said, "I give up. You're right, it's a lie. We stole the body. The resurrection's just a lie we made up. Now for goodness' sake cut me down from this cross, so I can get on with the rest of my life"? But none of them ever said that because they knew Jesus had risen.

'Some of the other disciples were beheaded, but if the resurrection was just a lie, don't you think that at least one of them would have broken down and admitted it? Lots of people die for causes they believe in. No one volunteers to die for something they know is a miserable lie.'

Anna said, 'Sorry Pete, but I think your idea is a non-starter.'

'At the end of the day,' Megan said, 'many people have been converted because they cannot believe that the disciples would die for something they knew to be a lie.[79] Over the past 2,000 years, this has been the single most persuasive argument for the resurrection.'

I'd already decided that I wasn't going to be taken in by any of this. We turned our chairs round because the next video clip was just beginning. It was all about the so-called resurrection appearances of Jesus.

When it finished, back in our discussion group, Rob said, 'OK guys, do you realise how much is now at stake here tonight? Most of you said that you were convinced that Jesus really did die on the cross. So, if in the next 30 minutes you are persuaded that Jesus later appeared alive to people, you've just demonstrated that the resurrection happened! That's a dead person, come back to life. And if Jesus' resurrection happened, if we've got any sense we'll all have to get on our knees and become Christians!'

I wasn't sure how seriously Rob meant this. It was probably some sort of shock tactic to drive the point home. And it certainly got Kate and Andy looking rattled. Anna, however, seemed worryingly excited by the idea. Suzie just stared at Rob, probably trying to put him under a spell, or imagine him naked.

'These resurrection appearances are just legends that grew over time,' I said.

Andy replied, 'That's what I said two weeks ago, but it turns out that the New Testament was written by eye-witnesses.'

'No, actually,' I said, thinking of at least one TV documentary I could vaguely remember, 'you'll find that it was hundreds of years later that this stuff got written down.'

Rob said, 'Pete, you may have picked the wrong target there, because our earliest record of the resurrection appearances in 1 Corinthians 15:1–8 can actually be traced back to within a few months of the resurrection.'[80]

We then spent the next ten minutes tearing into the bit of the Bible he'd just mentioned. The more we talked, the more interesting it got. What surprised me was that it said more than 500 people saw the resurrected Jesus on one occasion, which was news to me.

'I'd always thought that the resurrection was just a ghost story,' Suzie said.

The moment she said it, another idea popped into my mind. And this time, no matter what Rob said, I was sure that I was onto something. 'Not exactly ghost stories, but something more subtle,' I said. 'Hallucinations. I reckon what you're calling resurrection appearances were actually just hallucinations.'

Andy gave me a high five, and for the first time in the entire evening, it seemed that I'd found a way out of having to admit that Christianity was true. But Rob didn't look flustered. Neither did Megan.

Megan replied, 'We studied hallucinations in a psychology elective at university. And let's just be clear: for this idea to work we've got to say that all 550-odd people who saw the resurrected Jesus, on eleven different occasions, over a period of six weeks, were all hallucinating the same thing. That everyone who had meals with him, and those who said they touched him and had long conversations with him, were all hallucinating.'

'Well, maybe they were,' I said bluffing hopelessly.

'Well, we don't know of any other group hallucinations. As far as I know, only one person can see a specific hallucination at any one time. And there's no reason to think I could ever somehow produce a hallucination in you. Remember, the whole point of a hallucination is that there's nothing actually there. If I'm having a hallucination, it's all in my mind, so obviously nobody else can see exactly what I'm seeing. So even if two people did hallucinate seeing Jesus at the same time, for one person he might be eating fish, but for the other he might be flying through the sky.

'And let's face it, hallucinations are very rare. They're usually caused by bodily deprivation or drugs. If you ever meet anyone who's had a hallucination, you'll find it'll almost certainly have been caused by one of those two things. Are we really being asked to believe that over the course of many weeks, hundreds of people in various locations from all sorts of backgrounds and with different temperaments all had identical simultaneous hallucinations?

'And individuals who do hallucinate don't usually suddenly stop. The number of resurrection appearances, and the fact that the appearances came to an abrupt halt, make the hallucination theory even more unlikely.[81]

'Remember that over 500 people saw the risen Jesus on one occasion. Maybe it is possible for two or three people to share the same hallucination. But 500? Writing in AD 55 the apostle Paul says that if you don't believe it, you can go and ask them yourself, because most of the 500 are still alive.

'Remember, hallucinations can't be touched, but the resurrected Jesus was tangible. He ate a piece of fish[82] and on one occasion he cooked breakfast for the disciples.[83] Peter says that they ate and drank with him after he rose from the dead.[84] And he held long conversations with them.[85]

'Even so, because there's nowhere else to turn, you might think that the hallucination theory would find some supporters, but no one has ever seriously argued for it because hallucinations are restricted to individuals.'

Rob stepped in and said, 'The final nail in the coffin of any hallucination theory is that even if it were true, it wouldn't solve the problem. You see, if you were to reject everything psychologists tell us about hallucinations, and say that Christianity is based on mass hallucination, you've still got to explain the empty tomb. You've still got to explain why the authorities didn't produce the real body of Jesus. And, as we've already seen, none of the alternative explanations for the empty tomb work. The only one that does fit the facts is that Jesus was and is risen.'

I was determined not to quit. 'Well, there must be some other explanation,' I said.

Rob replied, 'OK, but let's just be clear what this other explanation will have to do. It will have to include the fact that Jesus died on the cross, that the tomb was empty, and it will have to explain why a vast number of Jews suddenly started doing something their culture prohibited – worshipping a man.'

'Why wouldn't they do that?' Andy asked.

Rob replied, 'Well, Judaism is what's called monotheistic. God is one and is invisible. So that rules out worshipping a human being. That would be idolatry.'[86]

Suzie said, 'But there must be something we're missing. It can't be that cut and dried.'

Rob said, 'Well, all I'd insist on is that if you do reject every piece of evidence for the resurrection, you've still got to come up with something to account for the explosive growth of

Christianity. If you had lived in Rome and you had to bet in AD 33 either on the Roman Empire surviving 2,000 years or on twelve Jewish fishermen taking the world within the next few years, you wouldn't have bet on the fishermen! Yet here we are tonight with half of you lot named after the fishermen.'

The evening finished with a final burst of video, which involved a series of lawyers swearing blind that the evidence for the resurrection would stand up in any courtroom anywhere in the world, and that the average jury would easily find enough evidence to return a verdict that Jesus rose from the dead.[87] This was a bit demoralising, because I hadn't got anything else to argue back with. Then just as I was about to get up from the table and admit defeat, Suzie rescued me. 'Look, I've enjoyed it tonight,' she said, 'but I just want you all to know that it's not for me. I mean, Jesus may be risen for you, but he's not risen for me. OK?'

Andy seemed suddenly animated by this. 'I'm sorry, Suzie, but that's absolutely ridiculous.'

'It's not ridiculous at all. It's exactly how I feel,' she said.

'But if you and I had been there on the first Easter Sunday and walked into Jesus' tomb, we would either have seen a body in there or we wouldn't. And if we'd been doubting Thomas as he reached out towards the supposedly resurrected Jesus, we would either have touched real flesh or we wouldn't. When they ate breakfast with Jesus, they would either have seen a real fish disappear into his mouth or they wouldn't.'

Dan chipped in, 'Suzie, can you honestly say that you would have left that tomb thinking, "Well, it may have been empty for you, but it wasn't empty for me"?'

'Well, perhaps not,' she said. 'But the truth is that I'm not interested in whether or not it happened. I want to know whether it'll do anything for me. Can I have an experience of

God, or of Jesus, or whatever? I'm up for it, if I can feel some-thing, if it will make my life better, or make me happier, you know.'

Dan said, 'Well, Suzie, that's the beauty of the resurrection. Millions of people are claiming right now to be experiencing a relationship with Jesus because Jesus is alive. I've experienced his love, his power, and I know what a difference it's made to me. The great thing about the resurrection is that right now we can test whether it's true.'

This sort of focused our minds, because there was suddenly a clear and present danger that Dan was going to ask us to bow our heads in prayer or something cringey like that. He continued, 'If you were on a jury and you'd heard enough evidence to convince you that the resurrection is true, you'd have to go back into the courtroom and deliver your verdict. But you'd be really excited about delivering your honest verdict if you could begin a relationship with God as a result. The point is that if Jesus is risen, we can meet him right now.'

There was silence. Everyone looked nervous, except Anna possibly. I was dying inside. Was anyone going to break ranks and jump into Christianity? Was Andy going to start a prayer? Was Kate going to join her brother? With every second the silence went on, I was more and more desperate for the ground to open up and swallow me. I could see Andy sweat-ing.

Finally Rob said, 'Let's just chill, and think about it for a week. We can come back next time and talk about what this kind of step would involve.'

We spilt out across the street to a chip shop. I could hardly believe that we'd all been to the brink and back. What was happening to my friends? What was happening to me? Surely becoming a Christian would involve giving up everything I wanted to do? But then again, I could hardly say that Dan or Rob or Megan spent all their time feeling miserable. I decided to forget all about it. I looked at my reflection in a shop window and mouthed a solemn vow to myself: I would retain my coolness even if all around me were losing theirs.

chapter 26

Mikey here again.

'Mikey, there's something I've been meaning to tell you,' Dan said. 'My dad's alive, and he's written to my mum.'

'You're joking me!'

'I found the letter hidden under her bed. And that's not all. You know she's got this boyfriend called Mark, who's living with us? Well, I've even begun to wonder whether . . .' Dan suddenly shut up. So did everyone else, because Anna was getting out of her dad's car. She looked awesome, which made me feel sick.

Pete, Dan, Kate, Suzie, Andy and Heather all looked self-consciously at the ground, expecting a scene. We'd been thrown together by the fact that anyone wanting in on the Malaysia trip had to learn to dive first. That meant freezing our whatsits off in a lake in Leicestershire for a weekend to get qualified. So we were all standing outside Suzie's house, waiting for our wheels.

Letting my heart rule my head, I went straight over to her.

'Anna, how are we going to make this weekend work if we're not even speaking to each other?' I said.

'And it's nice to see you too, Mikey. You never did have much of a way with words. Mind you, I suppose there wasn't much need for talking with Michelle Saunders. Straight down to business, was it, Mikey?'

'Oh, do me a favour! Can't we leave it out, just this once . . . ?'

'No, I'm sorry. There must be something wrong with me because I can't just leave it. Why did you do it, Mikey?'

'I dunno.'

'Let me down gently. Was I that boring?'

'Oh please! Look, it was just a spur of the moment thing.'

'And with Suzie? That was just a spur of the moment thing as well, eh?'

'It was a spur of the moment sort of life, Anna, but I've changed.'

'Oh yes, I've heard about this. Dan tells me that you've found yourself some morals from somewhere. About time too. And I hear you've told everyone you now believe in God. You're becoming positively angelic.'

'Well, you managed to keep your Christian background a secret from me. Why were you so embarrassed about it?'

'Look Mikey, we're both here for the same reason. We both want a month in Malaysia this summer for £500. But we're never going to hack five minutes together at this rate. So let's treat this as a trial, OK? For the next two days I'm officially making an effort, OK? I'll talk to you. I might even be nice to you. And, God knows, one day I suppose I'll have to forgive you. But to be honest, at this moment, I can't see how.'

chapter 27

Dan here. We're in a pub by a lake in a place called Stoney Cove. It's a disused quarry flooded with water. This is where you come if you want to learn to dive in exotic beautiful places but happen to live in Britain. It's either this or being sad at your local swimming pool. Mind you, this is March, and right now heated indoor chlorine seems very appealing. I can't imagine we'll be able to see anything underwater. I guess they've thrown a few shopping trolleys down there, but it must be pitch black.

We got here in two cars: one driven by Suzie's brother Jason; the other by his mate Alex. If nothing else, Jason has managed to convince us that this Malaysia trip isn't a wind-up. He showed us letters from the people he's got the funding from. And he's paid for this weekend. Tomorrow he reckons we'll be on our way to becoming qualified open water divers.

'What happens if I freeze to death down there?' Kate asked.

'Your dive buddy will come and rescue you,' Suzie said.

'What harm can you come to in seven metres of water?' Pete asked condescendingly. 'I'm not going to ponce around all weekend in the shallow end being someone's buddy. If I can give the instructor the slip, I'll be down the deep end by tomorrow night.'

'Well then you really will freeze to death, or drown,' Suzie replied.

'So what if I do?' Pete said unconvincingly. 'I've got nothing to fear. Remember, I haven't got religious mania yet.'

'You're not scared of dying?' Anna asked.

'Not a bit,' Pete replied instantly.

'I reckon you are,' Mikey said, 'and I reckon if your oxygen failed, you'd be begging for a dive buddy to save you, just like the rest of us.'

Pete said, 'You don't understand. I've got nothing to be ashamed of, and nothing to be afraid of.'

'So you'd rather not be rescued?' I asked.

'Dan, if I do meet my Maker, I'll be OK. I'm not afraid of dying.'

'I reckon you are afraid. And I reckon if you weren't so

172

concerned about your image, you'd admit you need Jesus.'

'I'm perfectly all right as I am,' Pete insisted.

Suzie asked, 'Dan, do you really think all seven of us sitting around this table have to believe what you believe or else?'

'It's got nothing to do with what I believe. It's obvious that we'll only feel the need for Jesus if we think we need saving. That's because Jesus is a saviour. That's what it says on his advertising. He does exactly what it says on the tin.'

Kate said, 'But I don't think I need saving. I'm not that bad.'

I replied, 'If you're comparing yourself to most other people then I'd agree you're doing fine, but if you compare yourself to God then that's a bit different.'

Anna said, 'OK, so how bad do you have to be to blow your chance of heaven?'

'Well, how high do you guys think the high jump bar is?' I asked.

'Well, I expect we'll all make it to heaven,' Kate said, 'because none of us have done anything really awful.'

'Like?' I asked.

'Like, you know . . . guns.'

'So murderers don't make it to heaven?'

'Of course not,' Kate said. 'Neither do armed robbers or even burglars as far as I'm concerned, but there are little sins which aren't that bad, like . . .'

'Shoplifting or lying,' Suzie said. 'I mean, we've all told the odd lie, and I'm sure that if God's really there and he's got any sense of fair play, he can cut us a bit of slack.'

'So lying's OK, but murder isn't,' Anna said, 'but what about something in the middle, like cheating?'

She didn't look at Mikey, but she might as well have done.

'Depends what sort of cheating,' Mikey said. 'There's a huge difference between at the one extreme . . .'

'All right, guys,' Suzie interrupted. 'Let's sort this out.

What's the cut-off point whereby you can do little sins all you want right up until the moment you commit this particular cut-off point sin, but once you've done it or anything worse, you don't go to heaven?'

It went quiet. No one could quite put their finger on it, and then, almost inevitably, Andy spoke: 'Serious fraud.'

We all laughed. It was typical of Andy to just sit there for ages and then come up with something like that.

'You see how funny it sounds when we try to be God?' I said. 'We decide: "All human beings go to heaven, except those who've committed serious fraud or worse." Who do we think we are? We need God to tell us what the cut-off point is.'

'So,' Anna asked, 'what does God say the cut-off point is?'

'God says we're all cut off. None of us are good enough. The Bible says that "all have sinned and fall short of the glory of God".'[88]

'What does that mean?' Mikey asked.

'Well, how about this for an example? Just think for a moment about that new tannoy system they've put in the corridors at school. Everyone in the entire school hears what goes out over those loudspeakers between lessons.

'How would you feel if all the worst things you've ever said about anyone went out on air? And what if your worst ever thoughts got broadcast on that thing too, so that everyone at school could hear what you'd been thinking?'

I paused. There was a silence. It lasted a very long 15 seconds. The atmosphere seemed to change very slightly, and then I continued: 'And what if the worst things you'd ever done got shown on that screen in the entrance hall? How would you feel?'

'Sends a shiver down my spine just to think about it,' Anna said.

'You see, we've all fallen short of our own standards. How

much more have we fallen short of God's?' I said. 'All of us have sinned and fallen short of the glory of God.'

Mikey said, 'This is a bit too close to reality for my liking, Dan.'

'Well, it's the ultimate reality TV.'

'No it's not,' Pete said, 'because it's not real at all. What you're talking about is make-believe. All that comes out on that tannoy is boring staff announcements and those twats who do the school radio.'

'Of course it's totally unrealistic for any human being to know everything we've ever thought, said or done, but it is realistic for a supernatural God. In fact, God knowing all about us and then judging us is what we'd expect God to do.'

'Why should I fear God?' Pete asked.

'You tell me, Pete,' I replied. 'If God walked into this pub right now in bodily form, how would you respond?'

'I've absolutely no idea.'

Anna said, 'You'd be down on your knees like the rest of us, Pete. You'd feel totally exposed and naked, and I'll bet you any money that you'd start to feel guilty about specific sins you've committed.'

'Perhaps.'

Anna looked indignant: 'What do you mean "perhaps"? Are you telling us that you could honestly stand up and look God in the eye, and say to him, "I deserve heaven. Let me in."'

'Perhaps not.'

Heather said, 'Hey, I don't think for a moment I deserve heaven, but it's my life and at the end of the day I can do what I want. I'm not going to be forced into anything.'

I replied, 'That's right. God won't force you. He loves you so much, Heather, that he lets you do what you want. But it's not your life. God created life, and at the end of each of our lives he's going to ask us to give an account for what we've done with it. The Bible says that nothing impure can ever

175

enter heaven.[89] And that means that even one bad thought is a problem. God is perfect and pure. He cannot compromise his standard of holiness. And we can't turn the clock back and magically make our lives perfect.'

'So where does that leave me?' Kate asked.

'It leaves all of us standing before a holy God when we die, hearing our sins broadcast. God knows all about us, and in our heart of hearts every single one of us around this table knows that we're not holy enough to live with a holy God, not even for a second.'

'So we all go to hell?' Andy asked.

'Well, we certainly can't go to heaven! The Bible says the wages of sin is death.[90] We disqualify ourselves from heaven by our sin, so we face eternal death. Eternal separation from God. That's what hell is.'

'That's outrageous,' Heather said. 'How could a loving God send people like us to hell?'

I replied, 'Actually, hell shows how seriously God takes our decisions. If we choose to live without God at the centre of our life, he refuses to overrule our decision. You'll be pleased to know, Heather, that God won't force us. If we really don't want God in this life, he loves us so much that he doesn't then force us to hang around with him for ever.'

'But there should be forgiveness,' Heather said.

'There is!' I said. 'But if you refuse it, then blaming God for the fact you end up in hell is a bit like blaming the doctor for the fact that you're still ill after you've refused to take the medicine he gave you.'

They were fascinated by hell. Of course it's a massive subject. We talked about it for ages,[91] and it ended with Anna asking, 'So is there really punishment and agony in hell?'

I replied, 'Yes. Hell is not a place where God sends people because they were pretty good blokes who were unlucky enough to not believe the right stuff. Hell is not filled with people who turned to God while they had the chance. God, like any just judge, must punish sin. And hell is one of only two places where God punishes sin.'

'Flippin' heck! Where's the other one?' Andy asked.

'The cross.'

Andy said, 'But I just can't accept that. How can another person's death on a cross so long ago have any connection whatsoever with me sitting here in this pub? It's irrelevant.'

I replied, 'Well, here's the connection. Just a few moments ago, most of us agreed that we don't deserve heaven. We're separated from God, facing death. We're under a death sentence. Sooner or later, we're going to die. So, Andy, would it be relevant if someone died in your place?'

'Yes, I s'pose, but how could that possibly work?' Andy asked.

'Well, at The Quest we tried to imagine how it would work. How about this? What if you were under a sentence of death in the USA? You're facing death by lethal injection – it's just a question of when. This year? Next year? Who knows? Eventually your moment comes. The prison guards lead you out of your cell, strap you down onto a bed and wheel you into the death chamber. They've cooked up all these toxic chemicals to pump into your bloodstream. And then imagine the guards feeling your arm for a vein. Eventually they find a juicy one, stick the needle in and switch on the machine.

'At that point, Andy, would it be relevant if someone came in the room and pulled the needle out?'

'Of course.'

'Well, that's what God has done. He's like the judge who sentences you to death at your trial but then enters the death chamber and pulls the needle out.'

'But I'd already have some poison in my bloodstream by that stage.'

'Exactly. What happens next is that the trial judge opens the door of the death chamber and in walks a younger man, a stranger, you've never seen before. He bends down, puts his mouth to your arm and sucks out the poison.'

'Er! That's gross!' Suzie said.

'Actually, this is tame compared to your average crucifixion,' I said. 'But then just imagine if the judge ordered the prison guards to unstrap you from the bed. You get up and give the judge a massive hug, only to see him sentence the young stranger to be strapped down on the bed instead of you. "Justice has to be done, Andy," the judge says. "And this young man wants to die in your place."

'When the lethal drug cocktail finally fries his internal organs, the young stranger stops shaking, breathes his last and dies. Then the guards tell you that the stranger was the judge's only son! The judge has left the room. You run after him, chasing him down the hallway. "Your honour, why?" you scream at him. "Why would you do this for me?" He replies, "Because I really do love you."

'You can't believe that the judge would love you so much that he'd sacrifice his own son for you. You collapse in a mixture of relief and gratitude. You don't know whether to laugh or cry. You've never experienced sacrificial love like this before. Even so, you expect the guards to send you back to your cell, but the judge actually picks you up and carries you out through the prison gates to freedom. You're free. You start running down the road, shouting for joy, kissing everyone you meet.

'A few hours later you're walking along the street, thinking about the stranger who died in your place. But then you hear a police siren and you feel guilty again. You think, "It was all too good to be true. Stuff like this just doesn't happen." But then the police car passes you by, and the penny finally drops as you remember that as far as the judge is concerned, justice has been done. They're not after you any more.

'That's about the best I can do, Andy, to describe what happened when Jesus was executed 2,000 years ago. That was Jesus dying instead of you. Jesus was your substitute. Somehow, when God looked down on his own Son hanging on a wooden cross, he treated Jesus as if he were you. In fact, God treated Jesus as if he'd committed all the wrongdoing of everyone who would ever believe. Jesus took the rap instead of you, Andy. And if you believe it, the barrier of sin will be removed, and you will be able to begin a relationship with God that will never end. The Bible says: "God so loved the world that he gave his one and only Son, that whoever believes in him shall not perish but have eternal life." '[92]

Mikey asked, 'But even if I believed that Jesus died in my place, I'm still guilty. In reality, nothing's changed.'

'No, you're not,' I replied. 'That's the beauty of it. By believing, you trade in your sin for Jesus' perfection. On the cross, Jesus took your guilt and gave you his forgiveness. You trade in your past for his future, your death for his resurrection and your hell for his heaven. Remember, he never sinned. He never had to apologise for anything. He was perfect in God's eyes, and the moment you believe, your status changes before God. You look as holy to God as Jesus does!'

Pete growled in total contempt, 'I'm sorry. I just find this embarrassing.'

Kate said, 'Either that or it's the most exciting thing I've ever heard. You see, unlike you lot, I live with Dan, and I know that he wakes up every morning feeling like a million dollars.'

Anna asked, 'Of course, and I would too if I could really believe it, because this is the impossible dream, isn't it? The idea that I can be loved no matter what! I've been thinking about this all week, because if God is real and he really loves me enough to give up his only Son for me, then I'd never have anything to worry about. I'd have nothing

179

left to prove to anyone.'

'More importantly,' I said, 'the moment you believe in Jesus, you enter a real relationship with God. The Bible says that "if anyone is in Christ, he is a new creation; the old has gone, the new has come".[93] It's the most awesome experience. It's better than sex!'

Pete said, 'Give me a break! I think I'm going to be sick.'

I replied, 'Pete, you know full well that last year I'd have reacted just like you're doing now. But the truth is that inside I was hurting because I've never known my dad. So I would have rejected the whole idea of God loving me, because I was trying to convince myself I didn't need a father's love from anyone. I was wearing a mask.'

Pete said, 'Dan, you're starting to sound like daytime TV.'

I carried on: 'Pete, the thrill of your life and the thrill of my life is relationships. It's what makes life worth living. We all know money won't do it. You want to be loved – that's what gives meaning and purpose and security to every human being. Jesus' death on the cross is such a big deal because it removes the barrier of sin, so there's nothing in the way. We can begin a relationship with a loving God. The verdict is in. God is real, and he's proved his love is real.'

Kate said, 'Dan, I need to talk to you about our dad.'

'You do?' I said, not sure what she meant. I'd have to ask her afterwards because Pete had already continued: 'Mate, I'm not wearing a mask and I'm not prepared to sign my life away.'

Andy said, 'Neither am I, but all this is making sense of one thing that has always bothered me. When I watch TV . . . well . . . I always feel blown away by nature programmes. You know, mountains, oceans, stars, planets. But I've always found Christianity a complete turn off. So I've never ever been able to connect in my mind God and Christianity, 'cos one seems exciting and the other deathly boring. But Dan, when you were talking about Jesus dying on the cross, I felt that sense of wonder again. You know, when you see a fantastic sunset, you feel a total buzz. That's how I felt just then. Jesus dying for me is a cool concept, but it can't be that simple.'

At that moment Jason and Alex came back from the bar. 'Who's up for some action?' Jason beamed. 'I've got you all invited to an insane scuba party. There's some mad Scots lads who've just left with a barrel of beer. I say we follow them.'

Moving outside we were swamped by a group of guys who seemed convinced that my sister was the missing ingredient in their social mix.

'I can't be doing with this,' Kate said. 'I'm not in the mood for being slobbered over. Take me home, Dan. I'm not diving tomorrow with a hangover.'

chapter 28

It was a top weekend. We went clubbing on Saturday night and the diving was fun, but I was pants at it. Anyway, apart from that Friday evening in the pub, there'd been no time to talk, as we all slept on the journey home. We got back late Sunday, and now it was Monday and I'd not spoken to Kate all day. I wanted to ask her what she was going to say about our dad, but it was 10.30 pm already and I'd seen her go to her room.

I knocked on her door and gently opened it. 'Katie,' I stage-whispered a couple of times. It was very cold. She must have left the window open, but I couldn't really see in the dark.

I went over to her bed in the darkness, and touched her

shoulder. Nothing. No shoulder. No one in the bed. I span round and switched on the light. She wasn't there!

The window was wide open. I looked outside and, blow me, there she was outdoors with her coat on, scampering across the street! She must have jumped down onto the flat back roof and gone out through the garden. What on earth was going on?

I'd caught her out, late at night, once before – that time we'd had our massive bust-up argument. And again, only three weeks ago, she'd come home after midnight, slammed the door and burst into tears, but she wouldn't tell me what that was all about. But now I was really suspicious because I'd caught her shimmying down the drainpipe from her bedroom window like a 14-year-old who's had a skinful of cider.

Was she on drugs? No. Did she have a new secret boyfriend? Possibly. But why should she keep it quiet after everything else she's told me? I was determined to follow her and find out. Apart from anything else, I was worried sick about her going out on her own.

I ran downstairs and grabbed my jacket and baseball cap. I wanted to be close enough to see she was safe, but far enough away not to be noticed. I wanted to find out what she was up to. I'd never followed anyone before, and to be honest I had trouble keeping up, she was walking so fast. I was about 100 metres back.

But when she got to the main road, she came to a complete stop under the streetlight on the corner, and just stood there as if she was waiting for someone. I stopped too, and kept my distance, hiding behind a phone box so that she wouldn't see me. Every time I looked, she was checking her watch, stamping her feet on the ground. Her breath was like puffs of smoke against the cold night air.

And then, on the other side of the street, to my complete horror, I spotted him. Nick Bailey, of all people! I just couldn't believe she'd got back with Nick after all he'd done to her. But there he was, creeping along. He seemed to be hiding as well. He was obviously trying to surprise her because every time she looked round, he ducked behind one of the cars.

I watched as Nick got closer and closer. He was coming up behind her. I wasn't going to just stay put and watch him put his hands over her eyes and say 'Guess who?' and all that lovey-dovey stuff. But then, when he was about ten metres away from her, I saw a flash of reflected light as he took his hand out of his pocket. He had a knife!

'Katie! Watch out!' I shouted at the top of my voice as a lorry went past, drowning me out. I started running towards her.

Then he grabbed her and held the knife at her throat! I heard her scream as he started dragging her away towards an alleyway. Then he got one hand right over her mouth and doubled her arm right up her back. He was frog-marching her off. I was too far away.

Suddenly she broke free. 'Dad! Dad, where are you!' she shouted.

She was calling out like a little girl for her daddy.

'Over here! It's me – Dan!' I yelled. By this time I was 50 metres away, sprinting as fast as I could.

'Daddy! Where are you?' she yelled before Nick slapped his hand back over her mouth.

I was cursing myself for letting this happen. She was cracking up mentally.

And then a car screeched up right in front of them. Nick dropped the knife and ran off. 'Oi you, come here!' yelled the driver in a deep voice. But Nick was gone.

Breathless, I panted, 'Katie, it's me!'

The driver got out of his car just as I arrived on the scene. Nothing on this earth could have prepared me for the shock. I looked into the eyes of my own father.

183

'That you, Daniel?' he said, as Kate ran into his arms.

I was in tears. 'Katie, is this who I think it is?'

'Oh Dan! Thank God you're here. I could have died.'

'Katie, is this who I think it is?'

She said, 'Oh Dan! I wasn't allowed to tell you, but yes.'

He looked nothing like Mark. Even after all these years, I recognised him instantly. Dad looked more like me than I did.

I walked slowly towards them both, seconds away from the first human contact I'd had with my dad since I was four years old. Then, almost falling over myself, all three of us hugged each other, crying.

'Dad, is it really you? Let me look at you.'

'It's me, Daniel. I'm sorry about everything. I can explain if you'll give me a chance.' He was much bigger than I remembered. Then suddenly it came to me. This was the man I'd seen Katie with at the train station two months ago.

'Katie, how long has this been going on?' I asked.

'There'll be time for that,' the driver, I mean . . . er . . . Dad, said. 'Let's get after that guy. Daniel, you stay here and make sure no one touches that knife. There'll be fingerprints on it. Katherine, get in the car. Let's get after him. Quick!'

'Dad, you don't understand. I know who it is,' Kate said. 'His name's Nick.'

'I don't care who it is. No one lays a finger on my daughter.' And with that they shot off in his BMW.

I was left standing on the street corner. A small crowd of people had gathered. I stood astride the knife, left on the pavement, bawling my eyes out. To the bemusement of everyone around me, I shouted out loud: 'Thank you, Lord!'

chapter 29

They failed to find Nick. The police arrived and took statements from all three of us. The knife was taken away for examination in a polythene bag. Shell-shocked, we sat in Dad's plush car at 1.30 am, making sure Kate was OK.

'Nick's been stalking me,' she said.

'What?' I said, spitting out a plastic cup of tea. 'You went out at 10.30 at night when you already knew some psychopath had been stalking you? Have you got a death wish or something, girl?'

Kate shrugged her shoulders. 'But I still can't believe Nick'd do something like that. I mean, threatening me with a knife, like a real rapist.'

We told Dad about the date rape, and it took him about an hour to finally calm down. I was worried he was going to find Nick and exact his own revenge, and not bother with the police and the courts. He was like a bomb with a short fuse. It was the first time I'd experienced his explosive temper.

Anyway, my dad had his own explaining to do – thirteen years' worth of explaining. But I'll give you a summary. He had been in New Zealand all the time, and he had sent us those birthday and Christmas cards. He said he'd written to Mum several times over the years, but she'd refused him any contact with us. There was some court ruling when I was five years old.

But living in Auckland, New Zealand, Dad had been sent the local newspaper report of our car accident last July by an old drinking pal who still lives round here. Dad had written to

Mum again, and finally she'd agreed to see him. He'd flown over, and the two of them had met up for 30 minutes. They'd had a blazing row, but Dad refused to fly home. He said he'd get a job and wait till I turned 18, when everything changed legally in terms of his access to us.

Anyway, Kate had rumbled what was going on in December, while I was still in hospital, totally ignorant of any of this. She had found the same letter under the bed and arranged a meeting with Dad without Mum knowing. Hence all the sneaking out at night.

'But Katie, how could you not tell your own brother what was going on?'

'Don't get angry with me, Dan,' she said. 'The day I arrived at hospital to tell you, you were being interviewed by that psychiatrist, Dr Alice Bennett. Well, I told Dr Bennett everything, and she said that you were highly unstable and "in a fragile mental state".'

'Oh, for crying out loud,' I said. 'What a joke!'

'Look Dan, you were in hospital, and the psychiatrist's professional opinion was that Dad being back on the scene might send you over the edge. Anyway, I wasn't even sure you'd believe me because . . .'

'Because I had to go back to New Zealand to sort out my business over there,' Dad said, wiping some sweat from his forehead. 'I'd left everyone in the lurch coming home to the UK at such short notice. And I had to sort out all my paper-work.'

Katie continued, 'So if I was going to suddenly tell you that Dad was alive and well, and that we'd had coffee together, I kinda wanted to be able to produce him in person, but he had cleared off back to the other side of the world. So I kept quiet, at least until Friday night in the pub. I never knew how cut up you'd been about it. Anyway, earlier today I arranged for Dad to pick me up on the street corner, precisely because we were going to plan how we'd bring you and Dad back together.'

'Hold on. One thing at a time,' I said. 'So Katie, that time I saw you both at the station?'

'Yep, I met Dad, but was under doctor's orders not to tell you anything about it. Remember, back then I thought you'd gone mad, Dan. I agreed with the psychiatrist. I thought if I told you about Dad your brain would explode. I had no idea what to make of you. It was only last month, when you suddenly started making sense out of my life, that my whole attitude changed.'

Dad interrupted, 'I hate to say this, but there's another problem. Look at the time. It's 2.30 am . . . your Mum's probably phoned the police by now, putting you both down as missing persons.'

I said, 'She's asleep. She must be, otherwise she would have texted me.'

Dad said, 'There's nothing else for it. We've got to go over there now, wake her up and tell her what's happened to Katherine tonight. She's got a right to know. But brace yourselves because this is going to be the mother of all confrontations.'

We drove over there, and very bravely Dad decided to ring the doorbell.

Mark and Mum came downstairs in their dressing gowns, and when she opened the door to see Dad standing there with us both, she let out a tirade of abuse. I'd never ever heard my mum swear like that. Mark looked visibly shaken.

It was hard work even getting a word in to tell Mum about the knife attack, but when she discovered that Dad had prevented a potential rape, she calmed down.

Mark looked as if he didn't really know what to do with himself. We sat down, all four of us as a family, plus Mark, in the front room. There was an edgy truce between Mum and Dad as Kate tried to explain herself.

I kept staring at Dad, at his nose, his eyes, his lips. I just wanted to touch him and make sure he was real. He did look a bit like Mark. It was well weird having Mark and Dad in the same room as each other. I guess I'd just put two and two together once I'd known Dad was alive and guessed wrong about Mark's true identity.

Dad eventually drove away at 4.30 am. Mum said she'd cry off sick from work the following day and take us all away to sort out how we were going to live the rest of our lives. I fell asleep on the sofa, simply exhausted by it all.

chapter 30

Six weeks later . . .

Well, we're a normal dysfunctional family again! Mum's constantly sniping at Dad. Her policy is still 'don't get mad, get even'. But amazingly we now see Dad every weekend. And with my eighteenth birthday just two weeks away, I'll soon be able to hang out with him whenever I want.

My dad has these massive mood swings, which makes him very unpredictable. He's like a child who never grew up. And yet here I am trying to relate to him as an adult. I can't really decide what difference it's made to me, having him back on the scene. He listens as best he can to everything I've tried to share with him about God, but he says things like: 'I'm not really a spiritual person, but I think you're doing your sister a power of good. She needs emotional support, Daniel, and I've never given her any all these years,' and 'Keep up the good work, Daniel' – which completely misses the point. But I do feel more complete having my dad around, which is cool.

And what's wicked is that most of my mates are edging closer to deciding to follow Jesus. We're no longer thrashing through the evidence for Christianity being true. They now tend to talk about what becoming a Christian would mean for them.

You won't be surprised to hear they've all asked: 'If I become a Christian, does that mean I can't have sex until I'm married?'[94] We had a big discussion about it, partly triggered by Heather asking: 'Are you saying, Dan, that it's not OK to be gay?'[95] Pete and Suzie in particular had obviously expected me to be a fully paid-up gay-basher. They seemed a bit disappointed to discover that I wasn't! Anna and Kate are seriously considering giving their lives to Jesus. The others are also counting the cost of what they'd have to give up.

Having said that, last week Andy asked a less personal question: 'What happens to people who die having never heard about Jesus?' We told him that it wasn't an issue for him because he had heard! Understandably, he wasn't satisfied with that, and Rob spared my blushes by giving him an answer that he seemed grudgingly happy with.[96]

For the last few days I've been pushing them a bit. They now know the score, and one or two of them have admitted that it's time for a response of some sort. The big ask has been whether they'd come to my baptism next Sunday night.

It's a big ask because although they've all been at least once to our church before, this time I've warned them that at the end of the talk, there'll be a direct invitation to come to the front of the building and pray to become a Christian.

I've been kneeling on my bedroom floor every morning from 7.10 till 7.50 for the last week, praying that they'll all turn up. I don't really think they all will, but who knows? I've told them it's decision time. And I've probably exaggerated how full-on the sermon will be to cover myself in case it's too in your face.

Will they all turn up and become Christians? Tomorrow night we'll find out.

chapter 31

It's Sunday 9th May. Exactly ten months since the car crash. Just over four months since going back to school and seven weeks since Dad intercepted the knife attack. (Oh, by the way, you'll be appalled to hear that it looks as though Nick might escape with a warning from the police due to insufficient evidence, but we're still looking for additional witnesses to come forward, because Nick has conjured up a false alibi.)

Kate's been in delayed shock about it all, but has rallied over the last few days, and is almost back to her normal self. She's a survivor! Nick and his family have moved away, which has taken some of the immediate pressure off.

I stood next to Kate outside the church building, wondering how many of our clique would pitch up.

Over the next few minutes, one by one, Anna, Andy, Heather, Suzie, Mikey and eventually Pete all showed. I tried to look laid back about it, but inside I was ecstatic. My prayers were being answered. I tried to imagine them all standing down the front at the end. I wondered whether Rob and Megan might have the privilege of praying with them to receive Christ. They'd met us in the foyer and sat with us on the back row. The place was packed. I was one of five teenagers being baptised in a transparent tank of water. We'd all been through The Quest course, and for a couple of minutes each we told the story of how we'd become Christians. I think I probably went on for about ten minutes, but no one seemed to mind. I didn't expect to feel anything special when I was actually dunked, but in some indefinable way God seemed even closer as I came up dripping wet.

It was an emotional experience for us all, but especially for me, because from that day when Mikey, Pete and Andy had come to see me in hospital I'd been dreaming of an occasion like this, but at several points along the way I'd thought this day would never come.

The worship time before the baptisms had been so powerful that the presence of God was almost tangible. I looked across at my friends, and Anna was visibly moved. I was sure she'd go forward. We had a visiting speaker who'd been wheeled in as a sort of specialist to present the message. He tried to be funny at the start, but it didn't work, which made me feel nervous. But when he got serious and told us that he'd be asking people to come forward at the end if they wanted to become Christians, he managed to create an 'atmosphere', if you know what I mean.

He paced up and down, and the more he went on, the clearer he became. He started to crank it up by saying: 'The result of the sins we've all committed is death. And the Bible says that one day, when we die, we'll stand before God and face judgement. We'll have to answer for everything we've ever thought, said or done. And if you think that God will just accept you as you are, then I'm afraid you've got another think coming.'

I couldn't bring myself to look across the row at what sort of reaction this was getting. I was just praying that they'd respond positively. He went on, raising his voice: 'Every single one of us in this building tonight will be there on judgement day, and the Bible says: "The wages of sin is death."[97] Jesus

191

said that death is "eternal punishment". He said it goes on just as long as eternal life goes on . . . for ever.[98] It's a place of "weeping and gnashing of teeth".[99] It's a place where the "worm does not die" and "the fire is not quenched".[100] Jesus used words like "agony"[101] and "torment"[102] to describe the sufferings of those who go there. But if you give your life to Jesus, you need never go to hell. Instead you will go to heaven. How come?'

He then went into the most tender description of God's love and Jesus' death on the cross. I thought that this would tip the scales for all of them – even for Pete perhaps. He finished by saying: 'God so loved you . . . you can write your name in there tonight. God so loved you that he gave his only Son, that if you believe in him, you won't perish, but will receive eternal life.[103] Nobody ever loved you like this before. God's offering you peace, forgiveness, security and an end to loneliness and stress. It won't be easy, but if you'll turn to Jesus tonight, you'll never regret it.'

He got us all to stand, and speeding up his delivery, he started revving up to ask people to come to the front. He warned: 'Jesus says that on judgement day there will be people begging him to let them into heaven, and he'll say to them, "I never knew you. Away from me."[104] He will say, "Oh, now you want me. You kept me outside knocking at your door all that time. You never let me in. We never got to know each other. You kept me outside knocking, but now you're dead, all of a sudden you want to open the door! No, it's too late."

'I'm asking anyone here who wants to become a Christian to open the door right now, while you have the chance. No one here tonight will ever be able to say that they never had an opportunity to respond to Jesus. God loves you and has a plan for your life. Won't you come?'

With that he stopped, and asked for people to go forward there and then to receive Christ as their personal Saviour.

I looked across our row at everyone's feet. I was too embarrassed to look up. No one moved. 'They will go forward in a second,' I thought. 'They just don't want to be the first.' Still no one moved. I thought, 'At the very least Anna will go forward, and maybe Kate as well.' But every single one of my friends' feet stayed rooted to the spot.

After 30 torturous seconds, and with none of my friends among those down the front, he closed with a prayer. I was totally gutted.

chapter 32

I told the others to go on ahead to get some coffee, and after five minutes of trying to pull myself together, I wandered out into the church lounge. I'd expected all my mates to have left the building, but they were standing around in two groups, chatting with some of the other guys who'd been baptised. Kate, Andy and Anna were in a corner together. I went over to them.

'Was it too full on? Too confrontational?' I asked defensively.

Kate said, 'No, he was only saying what you've already told us. And the music beforehand and all he said about God's love was really powerful.'

Andy said, 'I quite liked his sense of theatre. He certainly holds your attention, doesn't he?'

I had no other way of phrasing it, so I just came straight out with it: 'So why didn't any of you go forward?'

Anna looked embarrassed and said, 'Well, I know I should have done, but . . . er . . . I know this sounds pathetic, but I'm still wondering what everyone at school would think if I became a born-again Christian. I mean, I'm asking myself whether I really want to be the odd one out. Wouldn't I rather stay normal?'

Kate said, 'Cheer up, Dan. I can see the appeal of it all. What he said about unconditional love really gets me every time. That's what I want, Dan. But I guess where I'm probably at right now is that I also like having my own life and doing my own thing. I'm not saying not ever; I'm just saying not right now. It's such a massive decision.'

Deflated by Kate's response, I asked, 'What about you, Andy?'

'I wanted to go down there in a way,' he said, 'but I guess I'm still weighing it up. I mean, I've got my whole life ahead of me. But you've really opened my eyes to something, Dan. And maybe I'll turn to Jesus when I'm older. Maybe when I'm married or something, when I've lived a bit.'

Crushed by a ton of disappointment, I went over to Heather, Suzie, Mikey and Pete, hoping for, but not expecting, something better.

'Hiya! What did you reckon to that?' I asked. 'Too direct? Too emotional?'

'No, I liked his shotgun style,' Mikey said. 'At least he lets you know where you stand. It's better than vague wishy-washy nonsense. Sort of truth or consequences, wasn't it?'

'So,' I said, 'at the end of the day you don't believe Christianity is true? None of you believe it's true?'

'No, it's not that at all,' Suzie said. 'It probably is true. At least, I can't argue with all your evidence. And I think the stuff about God the Father's love is really moving. I could easily fall in love with Jesus, no problem.'

'So?' I asked in desperation.

'Well, there's so much to give up,' Heather said.

They all murmured in agreement, and then just looked at

me. They obviously felt that they'd made a considered and reasonable response.

'I'm sure we'll talk about it again sometime with you, Dan,' Mikey said, 'but as life's started to settle down again for me, I'm not so interested as I was, you know, a few weeks ago.'

Pete added, 'We were chatting about it before you came over just now, and we kinda feel that we've had enough for the time being. I mean, don't get us wrong, we've enjoyed the ride, Dan. It's been a real education, mate. But I think that's it – for now anyway. Sorry.'

Pete called Kate, Andy and Anna over.

Mikey said, 'We've got to go, Dan, 'cos there's a massive eighteenth tonight up in town. We're going to get taxis. Are you up for it?'

'No,' I said, 'count me out this time. Have fun,' I added half-heartedly as I waved goodbye.

'See you later,' Kate said. 'Tell Mum I'll be back before midnight.'

'As if . . .' Suzie laughed.

With that, the glass doors swished shut behind them. I went into the church toilets, opened a cubicle door, sat down, pushed the bolt across and let the tears roll.

chapter 33

'Hello, it's me. This is Suzie. Can anyone hear me?' I called out, as I opened my eyes for the first time, hoping a nurse might be passing my bed. Of course I was relieved that I was conscious and that I'd survived. I was flat on my back though. All I could see was the ceiling, which was bright yellow. I guess Malaysian hospitals must have yellow ceilings.

We'd left Heathrow on 31st July on a British Airways flight to Hong Kong and then flown Cathay Pacific down to the Malaysian capital, Kuala Lumpur. Dan didn't come on the trip in the end. He decided he'd rather go to some Christian event called 'Newday'. Heather also wimped out, saying scuba diving wasn't her scene. The other six of us arrived at Kuala Lumpur airport exhausted. But we knew that we still had one short connecting flight ahead of us to the coast, and then a boat trip which would finally end our 32-hour marathon journey to the coral reef.

Standing on the tarmac at Kuala Lumpur, I remember looking at that tiny Cessna aeroplane feeling worried. We knew that it was going to be a twin propeller job because my brother Jason, who'd gone out a week earlier, had told us. But up close the plane looked so fragile. And it was a stormy night, there were no other passengers and the pilot didn't speak English. 'I'm getting some bad vibes about this,' I remember saying to Andy as I buckled my seatbelt. I'll tell you what happened next in just a moment . . .

'That you, Suzie?' a voice called out from across the hospital ward. I looked up and there was Kate. Except she wasn't on a bed – she was lying on the floor. I pushed myself up and realised that I was lying on the floor too. I twisted round, and there, to my amazement, were Pete, Mikey, Andy and Anna all spreadeagled on this bright yellow floor, in strange contorted body positions. There was nothing else in the room, except us. And one closed door.

I was scared. 'What's going on?' I asked nervously. 'Why haven't they put us in proper hospital beds?'

'This is outrageous,' Pete said, picking himself up. 'What sort of a mickey mouse country has hospital wards with nothing in them?'

Then the atmosphere improved as Kate let out a shriek of

196

delight. She stood up and said, 'Oh wow, look! No injuries!' She was feeling her arms and legs.

It was true! Staring at each other we each came to the same thrilling realisation. 'What a let off!' Mikey said, jumping up and down, as we all began to let out hoots of relieved joy. I'll never forget what a fantastic feeling it was, as one after another we began to realise that we'd escaped without a mark on us. We hugged each other and punched the air. And then gradually, one by one, it hit us . . .

'But we couldn't possibly have survived a crash like that without so much as a scratch,' Andy said. 'So this can only mean . . .'

He never did finish his sentence, because we all heard the door click open. Spellbound, we watched a huge seven-foot man enter the room. He looked like a body builder, with luscious muscles faintly visible underneath a single white robe.

'Who are you?' Anna blurted out.

Nothing had prepared me for his reply: 'I'm an angel.'

'Oh no!' I screamed.

'Oh yes!' Kate shouted.

'Hey, this is no time for practical jokes,' Mikey said. 'The facilities in this hospital are literally non-existent. We want to see whoever's in charge here.'

'You will,' he replied. 'Come with me.'

He turned on his heel and went back out the door. Andy was already following him. At this point I thought to myself, 'Perhaps this is all a dream. It's surreal enough to be a dream.'

'Pinch me hard,' I told Kate.

'You what?' she asked.

'Do it now!' I ordered her.

She did and I felt a sharp pain.

The other side of the door was a sight that took my breath away: a huge panoramic human snake. I mean, a massive queue of people that stretched as far as the eye could see. And our leader, who called himself an 'angel', was taking us to join the front of the queue.

As we walked along, a huge stadium came into view, and we began to hear occasional bursts of cheering. Within seconds we were asked to step onto an escalator, which was taking people right up over the back of the stadium.

'I've had enough of this,' Mikey said. 'Will someone please tell me what's going on?'

Kate was the first one to utter the words out loud. 'We're dead,' she said.

As an insurance policy, I turned to Anna and said, 'OK, I give in. I accept Jesus.'

'Pardon?'

'I want to sign up. Remember what you said to me, just as we were about to crash?'

Anna said she couldn't remember a word.

Pete grabbed the angel and said, 'Look, I can see that you're real and I can feel that I'm real. But all this seems unreal. So there's obviously been some mistake. I should be stranded in a Malaysian forest with a parachute, or in a rescue dinghy, or in the back of an ambulance, or at least on a life-support machine.'

I said, 'Look, Mr Angel, I wasn't up for any of this. I don't believe in life after death, so I shouldn't be experiencing this. I should be getting a big fat nothing. I think there's been a mix-up. At the very least I should be reincarnated. That stuff happens, you know. I didn't vote for any of this. I was normal.'

The angel replied, 'I think you already know what's happening. Brace yourselves. This is it!'

'What is?' I asked.

'The final judgement,' Kate said.

We rose through a brilliant bright whiteness as the escalator took us up and over the back of the stadium.

'This is in the Bible, isn't it?' Andy asked.

'Yes,' Kate said.

The angel nodded in agreement, and as if reading from an invisible book he said, 'Then I saw a great white throne and him who was seated on it. Earth and sky fled from his presence, and there was no place for them. And I saw the dead, great and small, standing before the throne, and books were opened. Another book was opened, which is the book of life. The dead were judged according to what they had done as recorded in the books. The sea gave up the dead that were in it, and death and Hades gave up the dead that were in them, and each person was judged according to what he had done. Then death and Hades were thrown into the lake of fire. The lake of fire is the second death. If anyone's name was not found written in the book of life, he was thrown into the lake of fire.'[105]

I let out a scream, and taking hold of both Anna's arms I shook her as I yelled, 'For God's sake, I've changed my mind, OK?'

Anna had the same calm expression she'd had on her face as the plane had begun to nosedive. Of course, nobody knows how they're going to react in that situation. First everything's cool as you sit there flicking through the in-flight magazine, desperately looking for anything remotely interesting. And then you get a bit of turbulence, and you think, 'Well, it's a bumpy flight, but we'll be fine.'

I remember that Mikey was first to actually vomit. But as I was reaching for my paper bag and starting to feel I'd left my stomach behind, there was a loud bang and we went into a sudden spiral. I can't tell you how scary it is going down in a plane head first. I was yelling as those facemask things fell down and we all started putting on our life-jackets. And I just caught a glimpse of Anna's expression. She was totally calm.

The plane then suddenly righted itself – long enough for

me to look across at her again.

'Aren't you scared of dying?' I asked, almost angry that Anna wasn't looking terrified.

'No, Christ lives in me,' she said with a totally serene expression on her face. I think the way she said it had more of an impact on me than all the discussions we'd had with Dan, Rob and Megan.

And then the plane dived again, this time very steeply, and I remember screaming at Anna, 'Give me what you've got. Come on, quick!' But then I guess I blacked out.

But now I was standing on this escalator with a horrible feeling that I was about to see the whole set-up the angel had just described, and that I only had seconds left. I was still shaking Anna, 'Give me what you've got now!' I shouted at her in desperation.

She said, 'Suzie, it's too late. That's the whole point.'

I let go of her only because a floodlight was being shone right in my eyeballs and I needed my hands to deflect the blast. Totally bewildered, I had a feeling the escalator was now going down. Within seconds we touched ground level, this time inside a huge throbbing stadium. Gradually our eyes got used to the light, and I could see that the stadium interior was actually a courtroom. There was a platform at the front,[106] but whatever was on it was still too bright to look at.

'You're up first from your group,' the angel said to Kate.

Anna put her arm round Kate and asked, 'How do you feel?'

'I'm just glad I'm ready,' Kate said. 'It was only a month ago, but as soon as I'd done it I just knew I'd made the right decision.'

'How do you mean?' Andy asked.

'Well, the first clue was when I met my dad. I guess I'd always hated him, but when I actually met him again after 13 years, I just knew I wanted to forgive him. But I couldn't. I knew I needed power to do that. And that was partly why I started taking Christianity seriously. I could see that it had power to change people's lives, and I desperately wanted to be free. I mean, it does your head in plotting revenge on everyone all the time. I hated my dad, I hated my mum, I barely tolerated Dan and I despised Nick. I just wanted to be able to rise above my feelings, but I couldn't. I was trapped.

'And I just knew that there'd be some sort of release through Jesus. Some power, some connection. I guess I just wanted the chance to start all over again, and I'd got answers to the problems I had with Christianity. So about six weeks after that baptismal service when none of us went forward at the end, I knelt on the floor in my bedroom and asked God to take the sense of despair away. And the moment I did, it felt like a weight had been lifted off my shoulders. I poured out a long list of everything I'd ever done that I felt guilty about, and I could actually feel that coldness and aggression I used to have leaving me. I suppose I'm one of those Christians who felt different straight away. God's been so alive for me the past month, that in a strange kind of way this seems like . . . er . . . just what I always wanted.'

At that exact moment, the angel took her by the hand and led her out of the tunnel area where we were waiting our turn. When Kate stepped out of the way, the person on the platform came into view. A burst of sparkling light was coming from his face and his clothes. I could see him clearly in outline. He was a normal sized human. I just knew who it was, and I wanted to melt. I suppose I should have felt gutted to discover that it's all true after all – that you do meet Jesus when you die. But actually seeing him, I felt nothing but admiration. He looked so lovely and warm and inviting.

Kate stopped about 20 metres in front of Jesus, who was sitting on a huge white throne. There was a flurry of activity as the angel searched for a single book that he placed on the ground in front of Kate.

Jesus was looking down at another book, which he already had open on his lap. He suddenly looked up, and clearly recognising her he said, 'Katie, come, you who are blessed by my Father; take your inheritance, the kingdom prepared for you since the creation of the world.'[107]

And then there was a huge eruption of noise as all around us people stood up and cheered. By the time I looked back, Jesus had got what I can only describe as an Olympic torch in his hand, which he swung down to set the book lying on the floor on fire! This prompted more applause and chanting from the stands as Kate picked up what looked like jewels and was led off to Jesus' right-hand side.[108] She disappeared from view as a group of about 50 angels parted to allow her through.

The angel returned and said to Pete, 'Give them a couple of minutes, and then you'll be next.'

'Oh God, no!' Pete said, appealing to the angel. 'Look, there's been some sort of misunderstanding here. I'm sure that if we all just calm down we can thrash out some sort of compromise, because I'm what's called an agnostic. I didn't know that this would happen. At least, I didn't have total proof. I was keeping my options open, which was a pretty reasonable thing to do, given that I was only 18 and had every reason to expect at least another 50 years to research the whole subject further. So, strictly speaking, I shouldn't be here. I should have been filtered into wherever agnostics go.'

The angel looked genuinely sorry for him, but shaking his head he said, 'The Bible says: "Man is destined to die once, and after that to face judgement."'[109]

Mikey looked at Pete and said, 'You might as well give up. It's pointless.'

Pete slumped down onto the floor and began to sob. None of us could think of anything to say that could possibly cheer him up. Eventually he cried, 'Do you remember the last thing

Dan said to us? I cringed with embarrassment in the departure lounge at Heathrow as he gave us one of his Bible verses. Something about how you'll only find God when you seek him with all your heart.[110] Well, I never did.'

Andy interrupted, 'I think you're being a bit harsh on yourself, Pete. I mean, you were looking for proof, weren't you?'

Pete replied, 'I was just looking for an easy life. What's really upsetting is that Dan had actually convinced me that I was living by faith anyway. In fact, if I'm really honest, I'd even come to agree that I was taking a greater risk not being a Christian. I knew I was skating on thin ice.'

Pete headbutted the tunnel wall in frustration and looked towards Jesus. 'Now look where I am! There I was parading around calling myself an agnostic and saying that no one could ever know for sure whether God exists. But the truth is I treated the whole thing like I would a pub debate on whether or not the Loch Ness monster really exists. At the end of the day, what was going on in a Scottish lake was irrelevant to me either way, but any fool could see that if Christianity was true I was stuffed. But I just argued against every single piece of evidence.'

Mikey asked, 'But why? Why?'

'Because I was too proud,' Pete said, 'and rather than have to admit I was wrong, or that I needed forgiveness, I had the option of saying that I needed 100 per cent proof that it was all true.'

Andy said, 'And the irony of it all is that all six of us got on three different plane flights yesterday without a 100 per cent guarantee that any of them would land safely.'[111]

'Makes you sick, doesn't it?' Pete said. 'That proves I was happy to accept less than total certainty when it came to plane travel, yet after all Dan told us, and even seeing the change in Kate just in the past few weeks after our exams finished, I could see that Christianity was real.' He started drumming his fists into the angel's chest: 'Oh please, can't you stop this whole process? Am I really going to go to hell? There should be some sort of flexibility in the system for special cases like me.'

The angel said, 'The Judge will be in full possession of all the facts of your case. This is the last judgement, where absolute justice is done. No one will be treated more harshly than their sins deserve.'

And with that Pete was led up towards Jesus on the great white throne. I can't tell you how strange it was to see Pete Sykes and Jesus Christ looking straight at each other. Of course, at any other point in my life, the idea would have sounded ridiculous, but it was really happening and I was physically shaking in fear. Looking at Pete and Jesus it struck me that most decisions carry with them some risk if you get it wrong. Most of the time, the risk is trivial. The worst case scenario isn't too bad. But the decision about Jesus had turned out to be monumentally important. I was sure Pete was in for the shock of his life.

Jesus seemed to know that Pete's name wouldn't be in the 'book of life' that he had open on his lap. Not finding it, Jesus looked up with great disappointment in his eyes.

And Pete said, 'Jesus. Sir. First of all, I obviously owe you a massive apology. And I know it's probably not possible for you to bend the rules at this late stage, but compared to a lot of the people you must have to deal with, you'd have to agree that I'm not that bad. In fact, as I'm sure you know, I've been to church twice recently and had several long discussions about your . . . er . . . your claims. And this was all happening while I had my exams to deal with, so I do feel that should be taken into consideration. And I am really genuinely sorry, because my attitude has been very selfish. I don't suppose you could sort of adjourn my case while I sort of work my way into that book you've got there? I promise I'll try really hard.'

With an air of regret and sadness, Jesus said, 'I never knew you. Away from me.'[112]

Pete collapsed on the floor. A couple of angels carried him off to Jesus' left-hand side. In fact the visual impact of seeing Pete carted off in the opposite direction to where Kate had gone was the most frightening thing of all.

When the angel came back, I asked him, 'Pete's gone to hell, hasn't he?'

He nodded.

The other side of the grave, it just seemed totally logical. I mean, how could Pete possibly go to heaven? He had stubbornly resisted every subtle and every blatant offer of God's love. Jesus had left heaven and gone to earth to die to make a way for people like Pete to be forgiven, but Pete had even resisted that! I asked myself, 'What more could God have possibly done without forcing Pete to love him?' Pete had passionately wanted to remain independent from God his entire life. Now he'd got what he wanted.

But I looked again at the angel, and found myself wondering, 'What is hell really like?'[113] It didn't bear thinking about, so I tried not to.

The angel turned to Anna and said, 'Anna Edwards, you're next.'

Anna beamed like an excited twelve-year-old on a Saturday night waiting for the final of *Pop Idol*. 'I can honestly say I'm pleased for you, Anna,' I said. 'You must be ecstatic. I guess you just wanted Jesus more than we did. Is that it? I mean, you certainly went back to church, didn't you?'

'Well, discovering Dan's church was crucial. Because I just knew I had to go back after that baptismal service. I mean, you couldn't deny that God was really there in the worship. It was more than just singing, wasn't it? I just couldn't walk away from something as authentic as that.'

'Really? That's what swung it?'

'No, what swung it in the end was the crucifixion. They said on The Quest that life's greatest happiness is to be convinced you are loved, and all that evidence we ploughed through showed that it wasn't wishful thinking. God really did send his Son onto our planet in human form, and Jesus really had died in my place. I mean, what greater love could there possibly be than God sacrificing his own Son just to save me from what my sins deserved?

'And that was the end of all my insecurities. I mean, most people think they're stuck with their own character. Right? Wrong! I was insecure about everything: my face, my body, my weight, my clothes, even the way I talked. But I guess it must have been two weeks after that baptismal service that I eventually did go to the front of that church building to become a Christian. I just knew God's love was real. And Suzie, that ended all the stress. The battle was over. I'd won. I just relaxed. For the first time in my entire life, I had nothing to prove to anyone. Christ lived in me and God loved me, and I was going to heaven. I mean, that does kinda change your perspective on all life's hassles. There was no need to wear a mask any more.'

Well, she made it all sound so sensible. One thing still bothered me: 'But you'd always said previously that you were worried what people would think if you became a Bible-basher.'

'Absolutely,' she said. 'But in the end I found myself asking, "Am I really going to turn down the equivalent of a billion pounds just because of what other people might think?" And of course the irony of it all is that once I'd taken the plunge, people didn't reject me at all. If anything, it gave me novelty value. Now, I grant you, I had to totally rethink things as far as boys were concerned, but to be honest that was a blessed relief.'

I was now starting to envy her. 'Why didn't I join you,

Anna? What was I thinking of?'

She answered, 'I don't know, Suzie. We had a bit of a falling out, didn't we? But I just knew I had to make a decision. I just knew that there had to be more to life than what we had.'

I turned away as Anna was led off by the angel. I couldn't bring myself to watch as I heard the whole deal Katie got repeated behind me. I winced as I heard Jesus say, 'Anna, come, you who are blessed by my Father; take your inheritance, the kingdom prepared for you since the creation of the world.'[114]

When the noise in the stadium died down, I swallowed hard. There were only three of us left. I looked straight into Mikey's eyes, but it wasn't a romantic moment. You see, well before we left for Malaysia, both Kate and Anna had told us that they'd become Christians. And now, though it pains me to say it, they'd both gone to heaven. For them things were only going to get better. But Mikey, Andy and I were hellbound, and Mikey had been told he was next.

'I can't handle this amount of pressure,' Mikey said, sweating. 'Do you think hell really hurts? I mean, it's not going to be a bowl of strawberries, is it? I just can't conceive of something that never ends, but what else can eternal punishment be except eternal? It goes on for as long as eternal life, doesn't it? Help!' he called down the tunnel.

Andy bit his bottom lip and shed a tear. He said, 'Mikey, I honestly thought you were on your way to becoming a Christian. I mean, you started off as the most out-and-out atheist in the whole school, but after all that science stuff you really changed.'

Mikey said, 'But that's what's so annoying. Once I'd realised how strong the science pointing to God was, then I s'pose I should have searched with all my heart for God. I mean, think about how much progress I'd made. I knew by that stage that intelligent design was the only possible explanation for the existence of the universe and the existence of life, but in the end I failed to do anything about it.'

I tried to encourage him: 'No Mikey, you did do something about it. You talked about it endlessly to Rob and Dan, and you went along to The Quest and heard all the evidence. You didn't have to do any of that. That might score you a few points in the scheme of things. You never know.'

Mikey was inconsolable: 'Suzie, what you don't know is that on the night I split up with Anna, Dan gave me this Bible verse that's now coming back to me. He said that God had provided enough evidence through nature for any sane person to realise that God exists. But the truth is that I then suppressed it.'[115]

Andy asked, 'What do you mean by "suppressed"?'

'Well, that's the word Dan used – like when you suppress your feelings. I knew God existed, but since that baptismal service I've been sort of suppressing what I know is true. I just wanted my old life back – being able to do whatever I wanted without God or any hassle. I didn't want to think about how I might have to answer to God for anything, so I just deliberately forgot about God. It was easy enough. I blocked it out and hoped the whole thing would just go away.'

The angel took hold of Mikey's arm. This I had to see. If anyone could argue his way out of a tight corner, Mikey could.

It was painful watching Jesus look for Mikey's name in the book of life, and just knowing it wouldn't be there. When Jesus eventually looked up, Mikey spoke: 'Lord Jesus,' he said, 'all through my life I thought that if this moment ever arrived, I'd give you a piece of my mind and a volley of abuse. But now I'm looking at you, I just want to say that I feel different. I genuinely do think you gave me enough evidence. Enough for anyone to believe that you made the world and that you made me. And I don't have any excuse. I mean, it even went beyond the academic, didn't it? You gave me that amazing coincidence thing with me being caught on camera just like Dan predicted, and still I wouldn't receive the love you showed me. So I'm not going to be stupid and pretend I did get my sins forgiven. But I do want to ask . . . er . . . is there any other way you can let my sin into heaven? I mean, could you kind of section me off and create a bit of heaven that isn't perfect? Or better still, could you stop being perfect, perhaps? I know that's a big ask, especially coming from me, but I did at least believe that you existed. Is that enough?'

Jesus could hardly begin to look at Mikey. I remember my dad having that expression on his face, when it was obvious that he loved me, but that he couldn't bend the rules. It struck me as I looked at Mikey that his appeal didn't amount to much. Even the devil, who presumably must exist, believes that God exists. It wasn't enough.

Jesus said quietly, 'Away from me. I never knew you.'

Mikey didn't resist as he was led away. He did look back at us though, and then he looked across to Jesus' right-hand side where Anna and Kate had been taken. You're just left with such a feeling of regret. I guess that's what all the 'weeping and gnashing of teeth' in hell must be all about. A sense of 'if only'.

I was dreading the angel coming back. If Andy was next, that would give me more time to get my act together.

The angel put his hand on Andy's shoulder. To my surprise, Andy smiled.

'What have you got to smile about?' I asked indignantly.

'I think I'm going to heaven, Suzie,' he said.

'You what? How come?'

'Well, you remember the delay in the departure lounge in Hong Kong? Well, I finished reading that book – you know, the one with the prayer in the back that you're supposed to pray to become a Christian. Anyway, I got to the end and thought, "Why not?"

'I mean, I'd spent long enough sitting on the fence. And I'd asked virtually every tough question in the book, and I'd got answers, most of which were at least reasonable. I was just sitting there by the duty free shop thinking, "What have I got to lose?" Look, I know I'm a bit unusual because, to be fair, I've not really got emotionally involved. I guess Kate and Anna had hurts which they wanted God to heal. I reckon I must have turned to Christianity simply because it was so obviously true. I wasn't in any crisis or turmoil.'

'Flippin' heck, Andy! Why didn't you tell me?'

'Well, I didn't feel any different afterwards. I just read the book, prayed the prayer, and I felt exactly the same. I s'pose I should have got more excited about it, but for me it was nothing more than a logical, rational decision. I just couldn't get away from the fact that when you add up the evidence for God's existence in nature and in the moral sense we all have, and then you factor in the reliability of the Bible, the claims of Christ which leave you with nowhere else to turn and then the stone-cold certainty of the resurrection, I mean it's a pretty compelling case. I s'pose the one thing I had going for me was that I knew that if there was even a chance that we were on earth for a reason, then there was nothing more important than trying to find out what that reason was.'

'So you just said a 15-second prayer, and that was it?'

'Well, I guess I'm about to find out. But I'm not feeling worried about going up before Jesus. I told him at Hong Kong airport that I was sorry for my sins, that I was turning away from everything I knew to be wrong, that I believed he died for me, and that I wanted him in my life.'

'So did he come in?'

'I dunno. I didn't feel anything, but according to that book I read, the Bible says he comes in whether you feel anything or not. Let's see . . .'

This was totally unexpected. The angel led Andy up to the great white throne, and Jesus started looking through the 'book of life'.

And then, blow me, Jesus said, 'Andy, come, you who are blessed by my Father; take your inheritance, the kingdom prepared for you since the creation of the world.'[116]

I was gobsmacked. Simple as that! Andy jumped up in the air as the crowd rose to their feet. They celebrated just as much as they had for any of the others who'd made it. I didn't know whether to laugh or cry as Andy was led away to heaven. I'd thought there'd be some sort of coffee break to see if Andy's airport prayer really counted. Was his prayer long enough? Was it too recent? Would he have to prove he meant it? I thought he might be put on probation, or asked to work in the courtroom, sweeping the floor for a few weeks. But no. He meant it with all his heart, and apparently that was enough. To be honest, I was impressed by how straight-forward Andy's approach to the whole thing had been. He realised the stakes were high, so he just followed the evidence. And it led him to heaven.

So what? Now it was my turn. And there was no escape. The nightmare was about to begin. It really was a chance to take stock of my whole life. I'd enjoyed myself, but it had never really occurred to me to be grateful, or to ask God whether there was anything I could do for him. I suppose I knew he was there, but I just ignored him because everyone else did. My mistake was to back the majority view, just because it suited me. I didn't think it would ever come to this. And then, in a horrible moment, I remembered saying at Heather's house that if I ever did meet God, I'd take my chances.

Well this is it. And the strange thing is that actually I probably did want a God who would always be there when I needed him, who would always love me, look after me and guide me, and probably the main reason I didn't become a Christian was because I was chicken. I wanted the comfort of staying the same. Fat lot of good it's done me!

'Suzie,' the angel said, 'we can't delay things any longer. It's your turn.'

By this stage I was actually looking forward to meeting Jesus. Seeing as I was going to spend for ever without him, I was going to at least enjoy this moment if I possibly could. And when I got up there and really clocked him, it was so sweet. This was the face of the greatest lover in history, the most famous man ever, the champion of the universe. All the angels worshipped him. He was so pure – I guess that's the word – so refreshing. He was so different to anyone else.

Books were laid at my feet, but I was horrified to see that they had my name on them. You'd think I would have been curious to see everything I'd ever done written up – all my good deeds and all my sins there in black and white on the page – but the fact is that when you reach this point, your sin sickens you. I was never too fussed about it on earth, but now I was offended by my sins. My selfishness appalled me.

Jesus was going through the motions of looking for my name in his 'book of life'. Not there, of course.

I'd planned not to say anything, and at least depart the scene with a bit of dignity, but when it came to it, I couldn't stop myself: 'But Jesus, please. I mean, you've seen three of my friends go to heaven. Can't I somehow get in on their ticket? You know, er . . . Lord . . . how some people are distant cousins? Maybe I could be a distant Christian? You know, I really listened to a lot of what Christians said about you, and on at least two occasions I even read the Bible. I went to that Quest thing. I did lots of kind things for people, especially my grandma. And there were those charity walkathon things, and it's not as if I went around killing people . . .'

Then came the words I'd been dreading: 'I never knew you. Away from me.'[117]

The angel led me off to Jesus' left-hand side, and that's when it really began to sink in. My knees buckled. Whatever hell was like, it was going to be awful. But maybe I'd be able to hang out with Mikey and Pete there, and it might turn out to be OK after all.

Once we got outside the stadium, my heart sank. We were totally alone. There were no mates. No one at all. Flippin' isolation. The angel left me. No people, no love, no peace, no hope.

And I was left with a blank horizon and silence, until I began to hear beneath me a noise of some sort. It got louder. It was sort of eerie. A pathetic wimpering cry like a demonised child in a horror movie. And then out of nowhere an aggressive shouting match in a language I couldn't make out. The noise was ugly and deafening as it grew more intense. And then more squeals of agony as I span round looking for where all this was coming from. I felt the floor starting to give way beneath me. I could see a huge hole was being shaken open. The hole got bigger and bigger. There was nowhere left to run. This was the start of the rest of my life. I fell in.

what next?

Are you sure you're going to heaven? Do you have that certainty? If you're not sure, then you can be. In fact God wants you to be sure (1 John 5:13). But following Jesus is a big commitment and involves a real cost.

To become a Christian, you need to do three things:

1. Say sorry. Tell God you're sorry for the wrong things you've done.
2. Say thank you. Thank God for punishing Jesus rather than you for those wrong things.
3. Say please. Ask God to come into your life as you follow Jesus Christ.

If you are serious about living for God, then you could pray this prayer:

Dear God, I'm really sorry for everything I've done wrong. [Tell him everything specific you can think of.] I turn away from all those things, and I understand that by praying this prayer, I will never have to do any of those things again.

Thank you for sending Jesus into the world to take the punishment I should have got for what I've done wrong. Thank you that Jesus died as my substitute. Thank you that I can know that I'm now totally forgiven, because all my sin has been totally taken by Jesus instead of me.

Please come into my life now as I commit myself to following Jesus whatever it takes and whatever the cost. Amen.

If you've prayed this prayer and meant it, you really need to tell someone who is a Christian today, or tomorrow at the latest, so that they can help you further.

And please tell me too! You can email me at adrian_holloway@hotmail.com and visit www.theshockof yourlife.com.

If you're not already involved in a church, here are two other websites that will put you in touch with a good church near you:

www.newfrontiers.xtn.org/churches (the homepage of Newfrontiers)
www.eauk.org/homepage (the homepage of the Evangelical Alliance – click on 'church search')

And if you're ever in London, you can visit us any Sunday at ChristChurch, central London. For our meeting times and venues, go to www.ccl.uk.net

notes

Note on context of scientific quotations: Most of the authorities cited in notes 2–33 are not Christians, and a few are atheists. However, rather than commenting on an individual's religious position, I have let their comments speak for themselves.

1. Dan is talking about something that happened to him in my previous book, *The Shock of Your Life*. However, at the end of that book, on page 153, I explain that, strictly speaking, it's impossible for anyone to come back to life having been to judgement day, which is what Dan is talking about here. Matthew 25:31–46 is one of several passages in the Bible that make clear that the final judgement occurs after the return of Christ and after all normal life as we know it today has come to an end (see Revelation 20:11–15). At the final judgement everyone who has ever lived is judged together. The idea that anyone can time-travel back from the future to the twenty-first century is therefore the stuff of fiction.

2. The Second Law of Thermodynamics has proved a formidable barrier to atheists trying to escape the fact that the Big Bang theory looks like creation by God. For example, Carl Sagan suggested that although the universe is currently expanding, it will eventually shrink into a tiny speck only to then bounce back into existence. In this way, Sagan said, the universe is eternal after all, oscillating between expansion and collapse. However, the Big Bounce theory falls down on the fact that even a bounced universe would have run out of energy long before now according to the Second Law of Thermodynamics. Professor Beatrice Tinsley, of Yale University, says, 'There is no known physics to reverse the collapse and bounce back to a new expansion' (cited by William Lane Craig, *Reasonable Faith* [Crossway Books, 1994], p. 103).

3. We also need to be protected from ultraviolet light, infra-red heat and meteorites from above, and incineration from the earth's core below. The fact that our planet has these and many other precise features essential for life is astonishing.

4. Many Christians are struck by the similarity between the explosive Big Bang theory and Genesis 1:3: 'And God said, "Let there be light," and there was light.'

5. 'If the rate of expansion one second after the Big Bang had been smaller by even one part in a hundred thousand million million the universe would have recollapsed before it ever reached its present size' (Professor Stephen Hawking, *A Brief History of Time* [Bantam Books, 1995], p. 134).

6. Professor Paul Davies, of the Australian Centre for Astrobiology at Macquarie University, says the likelihood of the forces of expansion and contraction being as perfectly balanced as they are is like aiming at a target one inch wide on the other side of the universe and hitting it! (Cited by John Polkinghorne, *One World* [SPCK, 1986], p. 58.)

7. Cambridge physicist Brandon Carter confirms that if gravity were altered by a mere one part in 10 to the power of 40 (1 followed by 40 zeros) 'stars like the sun would not exist, nor, one might argue, would any form of life that depends on solar-type stars for its sustenance' (quoted in Paul Davies, *God and New Physics* [Penguin, 1984], p. 188).

8. Hawking, Lucasian Professor of Mathematics at Cambridge University, says: 'The remarkable fact is that the values of these numbers seem to have been very finely adjusted to make possible the development of life' (*A Brief History of Time*, p. 138).

9. A variation as tiny as one particle in 10 billion would have been enough to prevent our universe coming into existence, according to Dr George Smoot, head of the NASA COBE satellite team. You can watch an interview with Dr Smoot at www.daystarcom.org/interview. He says that his discovery of ripples of radiation from the universe's beginning was 'like looking at God'.

10. If the oxygen resonance level were only half a per cent higher, carbon could never have formed, and neither could life. When astronomer Sir Fred Hoyle, who did the pioneering work on carbon's formation, found out how unlikely the existence of

carbon is, he confessed: 'Nothing has shaken my atheism as much as this discovery' (cited by David Wilkinson, *God, The Big Bang and Stephen Hawking* [Monarch, 1993], p. 108).

11. Hawking, *A Brief History of Time*, p. 140.

12. Robert Jastrow, Director of NASA's Goddard Institute for Space Studies, says that the universe had a beginning, and that the scientific evidence now points towards creation by God:

> This is an exceedingly strange development, unexpected by all but the theologians . . . We scientists did not expect to find evidence for an abrupt beginning because we have had until recently such extraordinary success in tracing the chain of cause and effect backward in time . . . At this moment it seems as though science will never be able to raise the curtain on the mystery of creation. For the scientist who has lived by his faith in the power of reason, the story ends like a bad dream. He has scaled the mountains of ignorance; he is about to conquer the highest peak; as he pulls himself over the final rock, he is greeted by a band of theologians who have been sitting there for centuries. (Extracts from this interview can be watched online at www.daystarcom.org/interview)

13. See Sir Roger Penrose, *The Emperor's New Mind: Concerning Computers, Minds and the Laws of Physics* (Oxford University Press, 1989), pp. 339–45, quoted by John Blanchard, *Does God Believe in Atheists?* (Evangelical Press, 2000), p. 268.

14. Dr Michael Denton, Senior Research Fellow in the Department of Biochemistry at the University of Otago in New Zealand, says:

> We now know not only of the existence of a break between the living and the non-living world, but also that it represents the most dramatic and fundamental of all the discontinuities of nature. Between a living cell and the most highly ordered non-biological system, such as a crystal or a snowflake, there is a chasm as vast and absolute as it is

possible to conceive. (*Evolution – A Theory in Crisis* [Adler & Adler Publishers, 1986], pp. 249–50)

15. This assumes that the right combination of chemicals happened to be present on the primitive earth's surface. With exactly this assumption, in 1953 Stanley Miller made a name for himself with an experiment based on the idea that the early earth was rich in ammonia, methane and hydrogen, which he forced to react together by using an electric discharge simulating primordial lightning. However, since 1980, NASA scientists have demonstrated that the primitive earth never had enough ammonia, methane or hydrogen to amount to anything, and that inert gases like carbon dioxide and nitrogen dominated, making the spontaneous generation of life even more unlikely.

16. It is worth bearing in mind that one tiny human cell contains more information than about 30 different average-sized science textbooks.

17.

> More than thirty years of experimentation on the origin of life in the fields of chemical and molecular evolution have led to a better perception of the immensity of the problem of the origin of life on Earth rather than its solution. At present, all discussions on principle theories and experiments in the field either end in stalemate or in a confession of ignorance. (Professor Klaus Dose, President of the Institute of Biochemistry at the University of Johannes Gutenberg, *The Origin of Life: More Questions than Answers* [Interdisciplinary Science Review 13, 1998], p. 348, cited in Lee Strobel, *The Case for Faith* [Zondervan, 2000], p. 107)

18. In this scenario, Crick says micro-organisms travelled in the head of a spaceship 'sent to earth by a higher civilization which developed elsewhere some billions of years ago' (Francis Crick, *Life Itself: Its Origin and Nature* [MacDonald, 1982], pp. 15–16).

19. This concept has been called 'panspermia'. Michael Denton comments: 'Nothing illustrates more clearly how intractable a problem the origin of life has become than the fact that world authorities can seriously toy with even the idea of panspermia' (*Evolution: A Theory in Crisis*, p. 271).

20. Chandra Wickramasinghe, Professor of Applied Mathematics and Astronomy at Cardiff University, who worked alongside astronomer Sir Fred Hoyle, and is widely regarded as an expert on this subject, calculated the odds against life starting accidentally as one in 10 to the power of 40,000. Wickramasinghe says that is equivalent to no chance: 'I am 100 per cent certain that life could not have started spontaneously on earth.' He says that his conclusion had come to him as quite a shock, because he had previously been 'strongly brainwashed to believe that science cannot be consistent with any kind of deliberate creation'. He concludes: 'The only logical answer to life is creation – and not accidental random shuffling' (*Daily Express*, 14 August 1981, cited by Blanchard, p. 298).

21. Professor Walter L. Bradley, of Texas A&M University, whose book *The Mystery of Life's Origin* established him as a leading authority in his field, says of such attempts to provide a naturalistic explanation for the origin of life: 'Despite all their efforts, they haven't even come up with a single possibility that even remotely makes sense. And there's no prospect they will. In fact, everything is pointing the other way – in the unmistakable direction of God. Today it takes a great deal of faith to be an honest scientist who is an atheist' (interviewed in Strobel, *The Case for Faith*, p. 111).

22.

> The mathematical odds of assembling a living organism are so astronomical that nobody still believes that random chance accounts for the origin of life. Even if you optimized the conditions, it wouldn't work. If you took all the carbon in the universe and put it on the face

of the earth, allowed it to chemically react at the most rapid rate possible, and left it for a billion years, the odds of creating just one functional protein molecule would be one chance in a 10 with 60 zeros after it. (Walter Bradley, quoted in Strobel, *The Case for Faith*, p. 101)

23. On numerous occasions, Sir Fred Hoyle has said that the idea that life emerged through the random shuffling of molecules is 'as ridiculous and improbable as saying that a tornado blowing through a junkyard will accidentally assemble a Boeing 747'.

24. Dr David Raup, Curator of the Field Museum of Natural History in Chicago, said, 'We are now about one hundred and twenty years after Darwin and the knowledge of the fossil record has been greatly expanded. We now have a quarter of a million fossil species, but the situation hasn't changed much . . . We have even fewer examples of evolutionary transition than we had in Darwin's time' (*Conflicts Between Darwin and Palaeontology*, Field Museum of Natural History Bulletin, vol. 50, p. 25). For this and much other material related to intelligent design research, go to www.arn.org

25. The so-called 'Cambrian explosion' of distinct fully formed species is found in rocks said to be about 600 million years old. Palaeontologist Dr George G. Simpson says, 'It remains true, as every palaeontologist knows, that most new species, genera, and families, appear in the record suddenly and are not led up to by known, gradual, completely continuous transitional sequences' (*The Major Features of Evolution* [Columbia University Press, 1965], p. 360, cited by Joe Boot, *A Time to Search* [Kingsway, 2002], pp. 86–87). In other words, Dr Simpson says that the fossil record does not lend support to the Darwinian theory of gradual development.

26. 'The known fossil record fails to document a single example of phyletic (gradual) evolution accomplishing a major morpho-logical transition and hence offers no evidence that the gradualist

model can be valid' (Stephen M. Stanley, Professor of Palaeobiology, John Hopkins University, *Macroevolution: Pattern and Process* [W. H. Freeman & Co., 1979], p. 39, cited by Boot, p. 86).

One of evolution's leading advocates in the world today, Steve Jones, Professor of Genetics at University College, London, wrote recently:

> The fossil record – in defiance of Darwin's whole idea of gradual change – often makes great leaps from one form to the next. Far from the display of intermediates to be expected from slow advance through natural selection, many species appear without warning, persist in fixed form, and disappear, leaving no descendents. Geology assuredly does not reveal any finely graduated organic chain, and this is the most obvious and gravest objection which can be urged against the theory of evolution. (Steve Jones, *Almost Like a Whale, The Origin of Species Updated* [Anchor, 2000], p. 252)

27.

> The smooth transition from one form of life to another which is implied in the theory . . . is not borne out by the facts. The search for 'missing links' between various living creatures, like humans and apes, is probably fruitless, because they never existed as distinct transitional forms . . . no one has yet found any evidence of such transitional creatures. (Dr Niles Eldredge [of the American Museum of Natural History], *The Guardian*, 21 November 1978, cited by Blanchard, pp. 99–100)

Steve Jones says:

> As more bones turn up, the story becomes less clear . . . In spite of a century's claims of the discovery of 'missing links', it is quite possible that no bone yet found is on the direct genetic line to ourselves. With so many kinds to choose from, so few remains of each, and such havoc among the relics, none of the fossils may have direct descendants today. (*Almost Like a Whale*, p. 427)

This is hardly the message coming through to the average student in the classroom.

28. Stephen J. Gould, late Professor of Geology and Palaeontology at Harvard University, and President of the American Association for the Advancement of Science, said that the extreme rarity of transitional forms in the fossil record 'persists as the trade secret of palaeontology'. Niles Eldredge agrees, claiming a deception has been taking place: 'We palaeontologists have said that the history of life supports [the story of gradual adaptive change] . . . all the while knowing that it does not' (both cited by Blanchard, p. 108). Gould and Eldredge's response to the problem was to suggest that evolution developed by sudden and massive jumps from one species to another, rather than by gradual change.

29. Dr Colin Patterson, the British Museum's senior palaeontologist, said: 'Nine-tenths of the talk of evolutionists is sheer nonsense, not founded on observation and wholly unsupported by facts. This museum is full of proofs of the utter falsity of their views. In all this great museum there is not a particle of evidence for the transmutation of species.' Speaking in New York City, at the American Museum of Natural History on 5 November 1981, Patterson said:

Last year I had a sudden realization that for over 20 years I was working on evolution in some way. One morning I woke up and something had happened in the night, and it struck me I had been working on this stuff for 20 years and there was not one thing I knew about it. That's quite a shock to learn that one can be misled so long . . . so for the last few weeks I've been putting a simple question to various people . . . Can you tell me anything you know about evolution . . . any one thing that is true? I tried the question on the geology staff at the Field Museum of Natural History and the only answer I got was silence. I tried it on the members of the Evolutionary Morphology Seminar in the University of Chicago, a very prestigious body of evolutionists, and all I got there was silence for a long time and eventually one person said, 'I do know one thing – it ought not to be taught in high school.' (Cited by Blanchard, pp. 114–115)

30. Writing his famous *Origin of Species*, published in 1859, Darwin foresaw the problem when he wrote: 'If it could be demonstrated that any complex organ existed which could not possibly have been formed by numerous, successive, slight modifications, my theory would absolutely break down' (Charles Darwin, *Origin of Species*, 6th edition [New York University Press], p. 154). Dr Michael J. Behe, Professor of Biochemistry at Lehigh University, Pennsylvania, gives several such examples of irreducible complexity in his book *Darwin's Black Box* (Touchstone, 1998). You can watch Dr Behe talk about this at www.ucsb.edu/detche/video/biology/behe/interview

31. Even Steve Jones, one of evolution's most passionate defenders, struggles to envisage the sort of species transformation needed: 'To imagine from the behaviour of an eccentric bear that a whole race could, in time, be rendered more and more aquatic, till at last a beast was produced as monstrous as a whale, is a little much to ask even of natural selection' (*Almost Like a Whale*, p. 164).

32. If anyone doubts the determination to keep God out of the picture at all costs, they need only consult Professor Richard Lewontin, a leading evolutionary geneticist, who claimed to speak for many when he confessed:

We take the side of science . . . because we have an a priori commitment to materialism. It is not that the methods and institutions of science somehow compel us to accept a material explanation of the phenomenal world, but . . . we are forced by our a priori adherence to material causes . . . for we cannot allow a divine foot in the door. ('Billions and Billions of Demons', *The New York Review*, 9 January 1997, p. 31, taken from www.arn.org)

33. Interestingly, Jean Rostand, a member of the Academy of Sciences of the French Academy, and one of France's most famous biologists, came to the opposite conclusion: 'Evolutionism is a fairy-tale for grown-ups,' he said. Louis Bounoure, formerly Professor of Biology at the University of Strasbourg, concluded: 'This theory has helped nothing in the progress of science. It is useless' (quoted from evolutionist website www.talkorigins.org – you may want to compare this with www.trueorigins.org).

34.

> The conclusion of intelligent design flows naturally from the data itself – not from sacred books or sectarian beliefs . . . The reluctance of science to embrace the conclusion of intelligent design . . . has no justifiable foundation . . . Many people, including many important and well-respected scientists, just don't want there to be anything beyond nature. (Michael Behe, *Darwin's Black Box*, p. 193ff.)

Behe wonders if God may have stepped in to miraculously help the evolutionary process over the barriers between species. This view is taken by some Christians, and is called 'theistic evolution'.

35. Earthquakes, volcanoes, floods, hurricanes, tidal waves, avalanches, blizzards and plagues are just some of the many natural causes of human misery. But all of the above are vital parts of an integrated physical system, which as we've already seen is fine-tuned to an extraordinarily exact degree to support life. We might want God to tinker with this finely tuned system by, for example, abolishing earthquakes and volcanic eruptions, but if God did as we suggest, we'd only create other problems elsewhere in the system. Taken as a whole, the planet functions in a phenomenally efficient way because its physical systems are so skilfully interconnected.

36. Matthew 27:46; Mark 15:34 (*The Message* version of the Bible, translated by Eugene Peterson [Navpress, 1993]).

37. Qur'an 9:5. The Qur'an is divided into chapters called suras, which are subdivided into verses called ayahs. However, verse numbers vary slightly in different printings of the Qur'an. Even so, when checking a verse you should never be more than one verse away from what you're looking for.

38. Friedrich Nietzsche (1844–1900) became famous for declaring, 'God is dead.' Hitler was thoroughly impressed by Nietzsche's radical atheism and visited Nietzsche's archives several times. Hitler presented Nietzsche's books to Italian fascist dictator Benito Mussolini.

39. John 14:6. See also Acts 4:12.

40. Qur'an 4:156–58.

41. 'They do blaspheme who say: "God is Christ the son of Mary" . . . Christ the son of Mary was no more than an apostle' (Qur'an 5:73, 78). 'Such [was] Jesus the son of Mary: [it is] a statement of truth, about which they vainly dispute. It is not befitting to [the majesty of] Allah that he should beget a son' (Qur'an 19:34, 35).

42. Mohammed was born around AD 571 and died AD 632.

43. See notes 55, 57 and 58, for example.

44. See note 41 above. The idea presented in the New Testament of the Father, Son and Holy Spirit being three distinct persons, but nevertheless all divine and operating as one God, is considered by Muslims to be 'shirk', or the one unforgivable sin of setting up partner gods for Allah (Qur'an 4:48).

45. Christians deny this, using evidence such as that corresponding to notes 54 to 63.

46. Qur'an 4:156–58.

47. i.e. Mohammed.

48. 'And I heal those born blind, and the lepers, and I quicken the dead, by Allah's leave' (Qur'an 3:49).

49. Qur'an 19:33–34 is one of many passages in the Qur'an mentioning Jesus, and these verses are taken to be a reference to the future return of Jesus, his embracing of Islam and his subsequent death. Many Muslims believe that when Jesus returns, he will marry and have children, die and then be buried near Mohammed. Some say Jesus will destroy every cross, kill all Jews, convert the Christians to the true faith and then reign as King of all Muslims.

50. Qur'an 44:54, 55:56. See also Qur'an 88:8–16 and Qur'an 56:8–38.

51. Qur'an 9:5.

52. Qur'an 9:29. These verses in Sura 9 contradict the earlier statement 'Let there be no compulsion in religion' (Qur'an 2:256). In these circumstances, Muslims are instructed to obey the later command, which takes precedence over the previous one. The reason being that although the earlier verse was appropriate for the start of Mohammed's journey, further suras were added to address the changing situation. In this way, early Muslims spread Islam by jihad, or holy war. This remains the understanding of some Muslims today. However, another view of jihad is that it is an internal spiritual battle which has nothing to do with bloodshed and violence.

53. Qur'an 6:142 and 7:31.

54. Josephus, *Antiquities* 18.63–64. This is a tenth-century Arabic version of the passage, quoted in James H. Charlesworth, *Jesus within Judaism* (Doubleday, 1988), p. 95, cited in Gary R. Habermas, *The Historical Jesus* (College Press, 1996), p. 194.

Josephus also makes a later reference to Jesus when he describes how the death of Jesus' brother James was ordered by the high priest Ananias: 'He convened a meeting of the Sanhedrin and brought before them a man named James, the brother of Jesus, who was called the Christ, and certain others. He accused them of having transgressed the law and delivered them up to be stoned' (Josephus, *Antiquities* 20.200).

55. Tacitus describes how the emperor Nero was suspected of starting the fire that burned down Rome in AD 64. Writing in AD 115, Tacitus says Nero blamed the Christians to divert suspicion away from himself:

> Nero fastened the guilt and inflicted the most exquisite tortures on a class hated for their abominations, called Christians by the populace. Christus, from whom the name had its origin, suffered the extreme penalty during the reign of Tiberius at the hands of one of our procurators, Pontius Pilate, and a most mischievous superstition, thus checked for the moment, again broke out not only in Judea, the first source of the evil, but even in Rome . . . Accordingly, an arrest was first made of all who pleaded guilty: then, upon their information, an immense multitude was convicted, not so much of the crime of firing the city, as of hatred against mankind. (Tacitus, *Annals* 15.44)

This confirms that the movement was based on the worship of a man who had been crucified. Seeing as a crucified man was the lowest of the low in Roman society, the fact that as early as AD 64 an 'immense multitude' of people in Rome were prepared to die for Jesus requires some explanation!

56. Pliny the Younger was Governor of Bithynia in northwest Turkey. In around AD 111, he wrote the following letter to his friend the emperor Trajan. In it, he refers to some Christians he has arrested. Pliny is clearly perplexed that they sang verses to an invisible historical person as if he were a god. It reads:

> I have asked them if they are Christians, and if they admit it, I repeat

the question a second and third time, with a warning of the punishment awaiting them. If they persist, I order them to be led away for execution; for whatever the nature of their admission, I am convinced that their stubbornness and unshakable obstinacy ought not to go unpunished . . . They also declared that the sum total of their guilt or error amounted to no more than this: they had met regularly before dawn on a fixed day to chant verses alternately amongst themselves in honour of Christ as if to a god, and also to bind themselves by oath, not for any criminal purpose, but to abstain from theft, robbery, and adultery . . . (Pliny the Younger, *Letters*, 10.96)

57. Lucian of Samosata was a second-century Greek humourist. In one of his works, he describes the early followers of Jesus:

The Christians . . . worship a man to this day – the distinguished personage who introduced their novel rites, and was crucified on that account. . . . [It] was impressed on them by their original lawgiver that they are all brothers, from the moment that they are converted, and deny the gods of Greece, and worship the crucified sage, and live after his laws. (Lucian, *The Death of Peregrine*, 11–13)

58. The earliest part of the Jewish *Babylonian Talmud*, compiled between AD 70 and AD 200, is scathing about Jesus in several passages, calling him a false messiah who led Israel astray, performing miracles by sorcery. Sanhedrin 43a confirms that he was executed on the eve of the Passover.

59. The earliest biography of Jesus, the Gospel of Mark, was probably written around AD 60. That's about 30 years after Jesus' death. This seems like a long time gap by modern standards, but it's very short by comparison. Alexander the Great died in 323 BC and the two earliest biographies of him by Arrian and Plutarch came more than 400 years later, yet historians rely on them as trustworthy.

60. The earliest sources confirm Matthew, Mark, Luke and John as the authors of the four biographies of Jesus found in the New

Testament. All four are actors in the New Testament story. Matthew and John are two of Jesus' twelve disciples. Mark was the travelling companion of the leading disciple, Peter, while Luke travelled with Paul, who claimed to be an eye-witness of the resurrected Jesus.

61. This is contained in 1 Corinthians 15:3–8. See note 80.

62. See table below.

Work	When written	Earliest surviving copy	Time gap	No. of copies
Herodotus	488–428 BC	AD 900	1,300 years	8
Thucydides	c. 460–400 BC	AD 900	1,300 years	8
Caesar's Gallic War	58–50 BC	AD 900	950 years	9–10
Livy's Roman History	59 BC–AD 17	AD 900	900 years	20
Tacitus	AD 100	AD 1100	1,000 years	20
New Testament	AD 40–100	AD 130 (full manuscripts AD 350)	300 years	5,000 Greek 10,000 Latin 9,300 others

63. The above table gives us a chance to compare the New Testament to other ancient books that today are considered trustworthy. We don't have the originals of any of the six works listed here in the extreme left-hand column. But before they disappeared, the originals were copied. So historians look at the time gap between when the original was written (e.g. for Tacitus this

232

was AD 100) and the earliest surviving copy (the oldest surviving copy of Tacitus was created in AD 1100), which is a gap of 1,000 years. The shorter the time gap between the original document and the earliest surviving copy, the more sure we are that we've got an accurate copy of the original. As you can see, the New Testament does well by comparison. Its various books were written between AD 40 and AD 100. And there's no dispute that the earliest bit we have of the New Testament is dated AD 130. This is a fragment of John's Gospel, which is in the John Rylands Library in Manchester, England. We have large portions of the New Testament from about AD 200 and full manuscripts of the New Testament from AD 350.

Looking at the extreme right-hand column, the greater the number of identical surviving copies we have, the more certain we can be that what we've got is an accurate copy of what was originally written. For the New Testament we have a total of 5,664 Greek manuscripts, and these were found in locations all over the ancient world. The similarity between them and 10,000 Latin manuscripts and a further 8,000 in Ethiopic, Slavic or Armenian, means we can reconstruct the text of the original New Testament from these copies. The result, according to scholars Norman Geisler and William Nix, is that 'The New Testament, then, has not only survived in more manuscripts than any other book from antiquity, but it has survived in a purer form than any other great book' (Norman L. Geisler and William E. Nix, *A General Introduction to the Bible* 1968; reprint [Moody Press, 1980], p. 367, cited by Strobel, *The Case for Christ* [Zondervan, 1998], p. 65).

Summing up, Sir Frederic Kenyon, perhaps the world's greatest expert of Greek papyrus and the former director of the British Museum, said: 'In no other case is the interval of time between the composition of the book and the date of the earliest manuscripts so short as in that of the New Testament.' He concluded: 'The last foundation for any doubt that the scriptures have come down to us substantially as they were written has now been removed' (*The Bible and Archaeology* [Harper, 1940], p. 288, cited by Strobel, *The Case for Christ*, p. 63).

64. Dan doesn't quote the Bible word for word. But from memory he tries to summarise Mark 14:61–64 or Matthew 26:63–66 or Luke 22:66–71.

65. This is a summary of John 20:24–29.

66. When Dan says 'He points to himself as God on legs', this doesn't mean that Jesus went around repeating the phrase 'I am God'. If he had, Jesus would have been arrested and tried for blasphemy before he'd had a chance to get his message out. As it was, by using various means of saying the same thing in different words, Jesus avoided arrest for three years. For example, Jesus often referred to himself as the 'Son of Man', who is a divine person described in a famous Old Testament passage (Daniel 7:13–14).

67. When Jesus told a man, 'Your sins are forgiven,' the religious leaders of his day were furious. 'Who can forgive sins but God alone?' they replied (Luke 5:20–21).

68. Mark 8:31.

69. This is a summary of Matthew 25:31–46.

70. John 8:46.

71. Luke 23:34.

72. Matthew chapters 5, 6 and 7.

73. e.g. John 10:21.

74. *Babylonian Talmud*, Sanhedrin 43a says Jesus worked miracles by 'sorcery and enticed Israel to apostasy'.

75. For example, Jesus would have had no control over the place of his birth, yet it was prophesied just over 700 years before

Jesus' birth that the Messiah would be born at a tiny place called Bethlehem (Micah 5:2). Bizarre details were also prophesied; for example the exact price for which Judas would agree to betray Jesus and that the money would be used to buy a potter's field (Zechariah 11:12–13, fulfilled in Matthew 26:15 and 27:7). The Messiah's death by crucifixion was prophesied before crucifixion was invented (Psalm 22:16; Isaiah 53), as was the fact that the soldiers would cast lots for his clothing (Psalm 22:18, fulfilled in John 19:23–24) and that he was offered vinegar to drink (Psalm 69:21, fulfilled in Matthew 27:34). Jesus would also have had no control over the fact that a spear would be thrust through his side after death (prophesied in Zechariah 12:10, fulfilled in John 19:34), which was not normal procedure, or that his legs would not be broken (prophesied in Psalm 34:20, fulfilled in John 19:33). It was normal procedure to break the legs of those who were crucified on the eve of the Sabbath, to speed up death. In conclusion, the prophecies range from the coming Messiah's required family tree ancestry all the way to the exact time of his death (Daniel 9:24–26), covering the major events of the Messiah's life along the way. For a comprehensive survey of Old Testament prophecies fulfilled in the life of Jesus, see Josh McDowell, *The New Evidence that Demands a Verdict* (Nelson, 1999), pp. 164–203.

76. Matthew 28:11–15.

77. A Roman flogging was done with a whip of leather strips with bits of bone and glass in it. The flogging would almost certainly have sent Jesus into hypovolaemic shock (i.e. losing a large amount of blood). The gospels show evidence of this. The whipping would have reduced much of his back to quivering ribbons of bleeding flesh. In fact a third-century historian, Eusebius, described how so much flesh was torn away during a Roman flogging that it was sometimes possible to see the internal organs of the person being whipped.

78. Medical doctor Alexander Metherell comments: 'The spear

apparently went through the right lung and into the heart, so when the spear was pulled out, some fluid – the pericardial effusion and the pleural effusion – came out. This would have the appearance of a clear fluid, like water, followed by a large volume of blood, as the eyewitness John described in his gospel' (John 19:34–37). Unless John had specific medical training, which is unlikely, he would not have known that this detail is consistent with the fact that Jesus was already dead. Medical doctor William D. Edwards concludes: 'Clearly the weight of the historical and medical evidence indicates that Jesus was dead before the wound to his side was inflicted . . . accordingly, interpretations based on the assumption that Jesus did not die on the cross appear to be at odds with modern medical knowledge.' Both of the above extracts are quoted in Lee Strobel, *The Case for Christ*, pp. 199–204.

79. Also, if it was an invented story, they would never have invented the idea that women were the first witnesses of the resurrection, because in ancient society, a woman's evidence wasn't valid in a court of law. Yet the story they actually came up with was that women were the first eye-witnesses both to the empty tomb and to the resurrection. They would never have invented what they knew would be a potentially damaging flaw in their own story.

80. No one disputes that the apostle Paul, who wrote much of the New Testament, claimed to have seen the resurrected Jesus. In one of his letters, probably written around AD 55-57, he writes:

Now, brothers, I want to remind you of the gospel I preached to you, which you received and on which you have taken your stand. By this gospel you are saved, if you hold firmly to the word I preached to you. Otherwise, you have believed in vain. For what I received I passed on to you as of first importance: that Christ died for our sins according to the Scriptures, that he was buried, that he was raised on the third day according to the Scriptures, and that he appeared to Peter, and then to the Twelve. After that, he appeared to more than five hundred of the brothers at the same time, most of whom are still living, though some have fallen asleep. Then he appeared to James, then to all the apostles, and last of all he appeared to me also, as to one abnormally born. (1 Corinthians 15:1–8)

This passage presents several problems for anyone suggesting the resurrection appearances are more legendary than historical. First of all, writing less than 30 years after the resurrection, Paul reminds the Corinthians that they can test whether the resurrection has any basis in fact or not, because the majority of the 500 or so witnesses are still alive and willing to be interviewed. But for a number of technical reasons (William Lane Craig, *Assessing the New Testament Evidence for the Historicity of the Resurrection of Jesus* [Edwin Mellen Press, 1989], pp. 1–115), this passage is thought to contain a much earlier credal statement. It is likely that Paul picked up this list of resurrection appearances shortly after his own conversion (probably around AD 32) in Damascus or later when he took a trip to Jerusalem to meet with Peter and James (probably between AD 35 and AD 38). Paul describes this trip in Galatians 1:18–19. In either event there is wide agreement among scholars that this list of resurrection appearances was well established in the form presented above by the time Paul picked it up between AD 32 and AD 38. This shows that the resurrection appearances are as old as Christianity itself, and are not a much later legendary development. This shouldn't surprise us because the resurrection of Jesus was the centrepiece of the earliest sermons recorded in the book of Acts. For example, Peter kicks off the Christian church by saying: 'God has raised this Jesus to life, and we are all witnesses of the fact' (Acts 2:32).

Equally important in this passage are the reported resurrection appearances to James and Paul himself. Anyone reading the gospels gets an enormous surprise to discover in the book of Acts that the leader of the Jerusalem church is James, Jesus' brother. Until the resurrection, James did not even believe in Jesus (John 7:5). It seems that James was converted by this resurrection appearance. (Later, Josephus tells us that James was stoned to death for his belief in his brother, Jesus.)

Turning to Paul, Paul says his conversion was the result of a resurrection appearance (Acts 9:3–9; 22:1–16; 26:12–20). If the resurrection is rejected as unhistorical, some alternative explanation must be found for the exceedingly unlikely historical fact that James and Paul were key leaders of the earliest church.

(I am indebted to Mike Licona for help with the reference to Dr Craig's book. Check out Mike's website at www.risenjesus.com)

81. The resurrection appearances come thick and fast at the end of the gospels, until Acts 1:9, when Jesus ascends to heaven. It is also worth pointing out that according to the gospels, the disciples were not expecting Jesus to rise at all. The disciples were depressed and disillusioned at the time of Jesus' death. Like everyone else, they thought that anyone crucified was cursed by God. They'd all deserted Jesus, and were actually cowering in a room behind a locked door. And every time they were told Jesus had risen they didn't believe it. Yet suddenly, in the book of Acts, we find that they're prepared to go hungry, naked, ridiculed, beaten, imprisoned and be martyred. What adequate alternative explanation is suggested for their transformation?

82. Luke 24:42–43.

83. John 21:1–14.

84. Acts 10:41.

85. Acts 1:3.

86. The Jews had been promised a Messiah, but they expected a political liberator. They had never understood messianic prophecies in the Old Testament to mean that the Messiah would actually be divine himself.

87. Sir Edward Clarke, a High Court lawyer, said in a letter to the Revd E. L. Macassey:

As a lawyer I have made a prolonged study of the evidence for the events of Easter Day. To me the evidence is conclusive, and over and over again in the High Court I have secured the verdict on evidence not nearly so compelling. As a lawyer I accept the Gospel evidence unreservedly as the testimony of truthful men to facts they were able to substantiate. (Quoted in Michael Green, *Christ is Risen, So What?* [Sovereign World, 1995], p. 34)

Professor Thomas Arnold, Chair of Modern History at Oxford University, said:

I have been used for many years to studying the histories of other times, and to examining and weighing the evidence of those who have written about them. And I know of no one fact in the history of mankind which is proved by better and fuller evidence of every sort, to the understanding of a fair inquirer, than the great sign which God has given us that Christ died and rose again from the dead. (Quoted by Wilbur Smith, *Therefore Stand: Christian Apologetics* [Baker Book House, 1965], pp. 425–26)

Lord Darling, a former Lord Chief Justice and therefore the most senior legal mind in Britain, said of the resurrection of Jesus: 'In its favour as living truth there exists such overwhelming evidence, positive and negative, factual and circumstantial, that no intelligent jury in the world could fail to bring in a verdict that the resurrection is true' (quoted in Michael Green, *Man Alive* [IVP, 1968]). Lord Caldecote, another former Lord Chief Justice, said that the evidence was so convincing that he described the resurrection of Jesus as 'a fact beyond dispute'. For this and other legal testimonies see 'The Evidence for the Resurrection of Jesus Christ, Part 2: Could the Evidence Stand Cross-Examination in a Modern Court of Law?' by John Ankerberg and Dr John Weldon at www.johnankerberg.org/Articles/apologetics

88. Romans 3:23.

89. Revelation 21:27.

90. Romans 6:23.

91. When I start a friendship with someone, I probably won't agree with all their opinions. I won't understand where they're coming from on one or two issues, because I don't know their background. But I trust what I do know of the person's character enough to begin being friends. Once that friendship develops I may end up trusting them enough to back their judgement on things I don't fully understand.

This is one way of looking at how we, God and the idea of hell relate to each other. There's a good chance that God's perspective on some things is going to start out a bit different from mine. The best example is how I view 'sin'. When other people sin against God, it doesn't seem that serious to us because we sin against God too. And that's one reason why hell may seem an unfair punishment from our point of view. But it's important to remember that God doesn't want anybody to go to hell (Ezekiel 33:11; 1 Timothy 2:4; 2 Peter 3:9). And the whole New Testament is full of the love and mercy of God expressed through Jesus.

So what should God do about sin? There could hardly be a greater sin than ignoring God, to whom we owe every breath, every pleasure and every single second of our life. Yet we're all guilty of sinning against God. A just judge is morally obliged to punish sin, and if we object to him doing so in hell, what do we suggest as an alternative? Perhaps God should force everyone into heaven? Perhaps he could do this by giving everyone a second chance after death to accept Jesus on judgement day? (This idea assumes that God hasn't already done everything he possibly could have done to demonstrate his love through Jesus.) But choosing Jesus after death would hardly be a genuine choice. And anyway, God refuses to do this because he refuses to violate us and our dignity. People would choose Jesus, not out of any love, but simply to avoid hell. And it would mean that God was actually an eternal kidnapper who forced people to be with him for ever, who didn't want to be with him for the whole of their lives on earth.

It's important to repeat that people go to hell because they've sinned, and not because they were unlucky enough to not believe the right stuff. In this sense, God doesn't send anyone to hell; rather, people send themselves to hell. In Romans 1:18–32, the Bible says we ultimately become the decisions we make. Each time we choose our own way, we solidify ourselves in a certain way of life, independent from God, and hell is a fairly logical continuation. It's an eternalisation of decisions we've already made for ourselves.

Our main objection is that hell seems like an over-reaction on God's part. Yet Matthew 11:20–24 indicates that some are punished more than others, and therefore there is a sense of proportionality in God's justice. There is clear evidence also that children will not be in hell (e.g. 2 Samuel 12:23), and many respected Bible believing scholars argue that after a period of suffering in hell, God will annihilate or extinguish people. Although I do not take this view myself, it is certainly a possibility that fits some of the relevant Bible passages.

We must be careful not to reject the doctrine of hell simply because we don't like it. It may turn out to make more sense than we can currently imagine. (See also note 96. As to whether the way Jesus describes hell should be taken literally, please see note 113.)

92. John 3:16.

93. 2 Corinthians 5:17.

94. There's no doubt that many of us are put off becoming Christians because the Bible forbids Christians to have sex outside of marriage. So we think: 'Maybe I'd be interested in becoming a Christian, but I could never obey the rules. I could never keep it up.' In other words, 'There's no way I can suddenly stop doing things that I naturally want to do.' We imagine that God does little or nothing to help. Subconsciously, we think God doesn't really understand what it's like to be human, and although he's ever so keen to tell us what not to do, he won't actually give us any supernatural power to enable us to obey his commands.

But hang on a minute! The only reason we'd ever become a Christian in the first place is because we think God is real, loves us and has a great plan for the rest of our life. It is therefore totally illogical to also believe that God wants us to be miserable! Especially as Jesus says the opposite. He says, 'I have come that they may have life, and have it to the full' (John 10:10).

This may come as a shock to some, but God thinks sex is great. He actually invented it. He needn't have made it as enjoyable as it actually is, so he must have thought, 'What the heck. I love them so much I'll make sex fantastically pleasurable. I'm going to make it really awesome.' If you can dare to believe for a moment that God really does want you to be sexually satisfied, then there must be a good reason why he thinks the best place to enjoy sex is with someone you're married to. It's not that God has sexual hang-ups and needs to loosen up a bit. It's more that he's seriously thrilled with one of his most exciting creations: Christian marriage (see Ephesians 5:22–33).

Anyone who's had sex realises that something more than physical penetration is going on. There's some sort of emotional, psychological and spiritual dimension to it. Jesus said that it's 'becoming one flesh – no longer two bodies but one' (*The Message* – Matthew 19:5; Jesus is actually quoting Genesis 1:27). God knows that this dynamic, 'one flesh' experience is best enjoyed within marriage, and the most recent research surveys back him up!

So far so good. The problem for many of us is that marriage seems light years away. And how do we know we'll ever get married anyway? Which leaves us feeling we've got a mountain to climb, and we don't even know if we'll ever get to the summit!

Before we despair of the journey ahead, we must remember that first of all it's not sinful to be tempted. After all, Jesus 'was tempted in every way, just as we are – yet was without sin' (Hebrews 4:15). More importantly, once you become a Christian, God's power comes into you, and the whole deal changes: 'And God is faithful; he will not let you be tempted beyond what you can bear. But when you are tempted, he will also provide a way out so that you can stand up under it'

(1 Corinthians 10:13).

It's easy to think that not having sex until you're married will leave you with all sorts of frustrations and sadness, whereas being sexually active with at least one person (whom you're 'in love' with) before you're married is the best way ahead. But so many have found that the opposite is the case. Sex before marriage is not all it's cracked up to be, and both you and others may be hurt in the process. Because God doesn't want you to get hurt, he empowers you as a Christian to keep yourself for a future marriage partner. If you're thinking, 'Well, I've already blown it, so what's the point?' then don't worry, because once you become a Christian, the slate is wiped clean. And if we've had sex outside marriage as a Christian, then 'If we confess our sins, he is faithful and just and will forgive us our sins and purify us from all unrighteousness' (1 John 1:9). This doesn't mean you're technically forgiven but really you're still guilty. It means that you're totally pure – purified from all unrighteousness. Look at the compassionate way Jesus treated a woman who was having sex outside of marriage in John 8:1–11. Although others condemned her, Jesus did not (verse 10). He empowered her to live a new life.

The whole of the Christian life is an adventure. And it's impossible to live it without God's help, but if we will only take the first few steps in his direction, we'll be amazed at how God will make it more enjoyable than anything else.

95. Many gay and lesbian people emailed me having read *The Shock of Your Life* and each email was essentially the same: 'I want to become a Christian, but I dare not get involved in church because I know they'll reject me because I'm gay. I can't stop being gay, so I'm stuck. Can you help?'

The idea that homosexual people aren't welcome in the Christian church is created partly by the media, who often give the impression that Christians basically get their kicks by persecuting homosexuals at any and every opportunity. In my experience, nothing could be further from the truth. The church is actually a place where people of every race, language, background and

243

sexual orientation are accepted equally because God loves people unconditionally. He loves gay and straight people just the same.

However, if we choose to follow Christ, we are choosing to live the way God wants us to live. And as described in the note above, God has good reasons for wanting us to enjoy sex only inside a marriage relationship. It's not that God is obsessively angry about homosexual sex. In fact it's hardly mentioned in the Bible. The big deal is that God says that any sex outside marriage is wrong. For example, when the apostle Paul wrote to a church in a city where homosexuality was widespread, he said:

> Now getting down to the questions you asked in your letter to me. First, is it a good thing to have sexual relations? Certainly – but only within a certain context. It's good for a man to have a wife, and for a woman to have a husband. Sexual drives are strong, but marriage is strong enough to contain them and provide for a balanced and fulfilling life in a world of sexual disorder. (*The Message* – 1 Corinthians 7:1–3)

Contrary to popular belief, the Bible does not condemn anyone for being homosexual. You might just as well say that the Bible condemns people for being heterosexual. It's what we do with our sexual urges that matters, and in this respect gay and straight people are in the same boat (see note 94).

The real issue is that for the homosexual, a straight marriage doesn't just seem like a dim and distant future hope; it looks like an out and out impossibility. It feels no more appealing than offering a straight teenager the dream of a gay marriage one day. It's also true that on the few occasions when the act of homosexual sex is mentioned in the Bible it is clearly described as unnatural and wrong (e.g. Romans 1:24–27).

At this point it is tempting to quote all those homosexual people we know who, having become Christians, have found to their delight (and sometimes surprise) a totally fulfilling sexual life within a straight marriage. These people can honestly say that they are not in denial or repressed. They do not feel that anyone's forced them into anything, but they have felt God transform them as people. One result of being born again for them has been a genuine change in the direction of their sexual desires. But typically these stories just make us feel worse, and occasionally angry. 'Maybe they weren't really gay in the first place' or 'I can't change who I am, and why should I have to change anyway?' are understandable reactions.

In this short note I can't do justice to this huge subject which is so personal to so many people. But I can offer this encouragement. When becoming a Christian, what we receive is not so much a system of rules which rule out certain types of people, but a person. We enter a relationship with Jesus. Jesus is for us, not against us. When Jesus encountered someone who'd done something that was considered to be sexually sinful, he managed to leave her feeling accepted and empowered (John 8:1–11). Seeing as he'd never sinned himself, Jesus was the one person who could have given her a hard time, but he was the one person who didn't. This is the God who loves us more than anyone else ever has or ever will. Jesus left her with hope, and he does the same today for everyone who comes to him.

96. We may be troubled by this question, partly because we feel that hell is an over-the-top punishment even for those who have consciously and deliberately rejected Jesus. If so, it may be helpful to read notes 91 and 113 before continuing.

With the question 'What about those who've never heard the good news about Jesus?' it's important to work from the clear to the unclear. Here are five clear principles that affect my attempt to answer it:

(a) We often ask this question because we're worried that such people might suffer an eternal injustice. So let's just consider the worst case scenario: someone goes to hell that we don't think should go to hell. But before we condemn God as unfair, there's got to be a chance that I don't know the full story and God does. My first principle therefore is that when answering a difficult question like this one, it's going to be important to remember that my perspective is a bit more limited than God's.

(b) There's nothing in the New Testament to suggest that Jesus is ultimately going to turn out to be a 'nasty piece of work' in the way he judges people. The whole Bible affirms that everyone will be judged absolutely fairly and without favouritism (Romans 2:11).

(c) There's no way that anyone can ever earn their way into heaven by being good enough. Jesus is the only person who has ever lived a perfect life, and therefore we need the covering of his unique perfection if we're ever going to get into heaven. There's no other way in (John 14:6; Acts 4:12). Otherwise heaven would become polluted (Revelation 21:27).

(d) No one can offer the excuse that they never knew about God, because God has clearly revealed himself in nature (Romans 1:19–20) and through our conscience (Romans 2:15–16). And no one will be able to offer the excuse that they happened to be born in the 'wrong' place. Acts 17:26–27 makes it clear that it doesn't matter where you live. God still reaches out to you in order for you to be saved.

(e) But the amount of information you need to know about Jesus in order to be 'saved' may vary widely. Some Muslims, for example, are converted without ever having met a Christian. They tell of how they encountered Jesus through dreams. Islam has an amazing doctrine of angels, dreams and visions, and God seems to use this to reveal Jesus to people living in some countries where there are relatively few Christians. In fact, one of India's most famous Christians, Sundar Singh, was converted from Sikhism in this way.

Beyond this we cannot say anything for definite because the Bible goes no further. Perhaps when people respond to the truth they have received (even through a different religion), God gives them more, and if they continue to respond, he will eventually send them the good news about Jesus.

Some have speculated that because some people in the Old

Testament were saved even without hearing Jesus' name, huge numbers of people who've never heard of Jesus will be saved anyway. But this idea seems to be at odds with the clear thrust of the New Testament, which is that everyone without a conscious commitment to Christ is in danger of perishing and that's why Christians are so urgently commanded to tell others (e.g. Jude 23). It also leads to the ridiculous situation whereby Christians could be making things worse for non-Christians by telling them the good news about Jesus (i.e. because if they then reject Jesus they're definitely lost, whereas previously they were likely to go to heaven because they'd 'never heard' the good news).

If we're unhappy with this answer, we may have to suspend judgement on this question for the time being, and have another crack at it later, when some of the related issues have become clearer. Remember, becoming a Christian is about starting a relationship with Jesus, not about understanding every single bit of Christianity on day one.

97. Romans 6:23.

98. Matthew 26:46. This verse presents a problem for anyone wanting to argue that although eternal life goes on for ever, eternal punishment does not. Here, the same Greek word (translated 'eternal') is used to describe the duration of eternal life and eternal punishment.

99. This phrase appears six times in Matthew's Gospel alone (8:12; 13:42; 13:50; 22:13; 24:51; 25:30).

100. Mark 9:48.

101. Luke 16:24–25.

102. Luke 16:23, 28.

103. John 3:16.

104. Matthew 7:23.

105. Revelation 20:11–15.

106. A raised platform, or judge's bench, is suggested by the original Greek of 2 Corinthians 5:10, which says, 'For we must all appear before the judgment seat of Christ, that each one may receive what is due to him for the things done while in the body, whether good or bad.'

107. Matthew 25:34.

108. The scene described here reflects the biblical data on judgement day, which is explained in much greater detail in *The Shock of Your Life*. The crowd in the stadium reflects the fact that Christians help in the work of judgement (1 Corinthians 6:2–3; Revelation 20:4). The fire which reveals costly stones, as some sort of appraisal of the Christian's life, reflects 1 Corinthians 3:12–15, one of many passages in the New Testament where rewards are mentioned for Christians on judgement day. The fact that Kate goes to Jesus' right-hand side reflects Matthew 25:31–33, which says,

> When the Son of Man comes in his glory, and all the angels with him, he will sit on his throne in heavenly glory. All the nations will be gathered before him, and he will separate the people one from another as a shepherd separates the sheep from the goats. He will put the sheep on his right and the goats on his left.

109. Hebrews 9:27.

110. Jeremiah 29:13.

111. It probably wouldn't feel like 'yesterday', however, because there is a time gap between death and the final judgement. This begs the question: what happens to us in between times?
The Bible does not teach that when we die we go straight to

the final judgement. Neither does the Bible teach that when we die we experience 'soul sleep', during which we're not conscious of anything until we're woken up by the final judgement.

In fact the Bible teaches that after death Christians are immediately in the presence of the Lord. This was certainly Paul's expectation (2 Corinthians 5:8; Philippians 1:23). And Jesus himself promised the thief on the cross: 'I tell you the truth, today you will be with me in paradise' (Luke 23:43). Some theologians have therefore called this intermediate state 'paradise' rather than 'heaven'.

You may find the diagram below helpful. It is a very simplified view of the New Testament's teaching about what happens to us when we die.

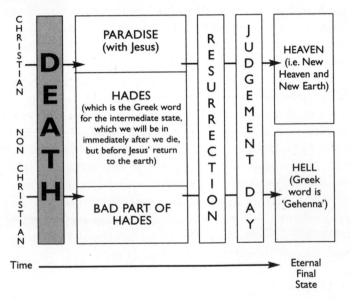

Freely adapted from David Lawrence, *Heaven . . . It's Not the End of the World* (Scripture Union, 1995), this diagram is explained more fully in *The Shock of Your Life*, pp. 149–53.

112. Matthew 7:23.

113. The question here is, 'Are the images Jesus uses to describe

hell, such as fire, physical or just symbolic?' When he's talking about people being thrown into hell in Mark 9:43–48, for example, Jesus makes clear that 'the fire never goes out'. But in Matthew 8:12 and 22:13, he talks about being thrown 'into the darkness, where there will be weeping and gnashing of teeth'. So is hell dark, or lit up by fire? The answer is that we don't know. The danger is that if we take the easy option and discount all the ghastly images as no more than symbolic, we run the risk of making Jesus into a scaremonger; that is, someone who went around deliberately exaggerating the horrors of hell just to frighten people into thinking that it's more painful than it actually is. Whatever the reality of suffering in hell, it must be equal to Jesus' dreadful descriptions of it. Perhaps the 'agony' (Luke 16:24), for example, is more mental than physical, but it must be agony nonetheless if we're not going to call Jesus a liar.

This, of course, doesn't help one bit in terms of our attempts to cope emotionally with the idea that anyone (especially those we love) might end up in hell. However, the Bible reassures us that God is absolutely just and fair (Genesis 18:25; Deuteronomy 32:4; Psalm 9:8; Romans 2:11). Furthermore, it seems that those who go to hell suffer different degrees of punishment there, and it will be more bearable for some than for others (Matthew 10:15; 11:22–24) and some will suffer less than others (Luke 12:47–48). And when we come to think about those who've already died, we may find that a surprising number of people turned to Christ on their deathbeds. We know that a simple but earnest plea at the last minute from the thief on the cross prompted Jesus to reply, 'Today you will be with me in paradise' (Luke 23:43).

114. Matthew 25:34.

115. Romans 1:18–20.

116. Matthew 25:34.

117. Matthew 7:23.

the shock of your life

by Adrian Holloway

www.theshockofyourlife.com

Dan, Becky and Emma have
one thing in common.
They just died. Were
they ready?

Buy the book and
visit the web site.

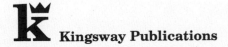

Kingsway Publications

Other Survivor books include . . .

Red Moon Rising by **Pete Greig** – 24-7 is at the centre of a prayer revival across the globe and this book gives a fantastic insight into what God is doing with ordinary prayer warriors.

Passion for Your Name by **Tim Hughes** – To read this book is to share in a journey of discovery, of truths encountered, principles gleaned, mistakes made and lessons learned. A valuable companion for all worshippers!

The Unquenchable Worshipper by **Matt Redman** – This book is about a kind of worshipper. Unquenchable. Undivided. Unpredictable. On a quest to bring glory and pleasure to God, these worshippers will not allow themselves to be distracted or defeated. They long for their hearts, lives and songs to be the kind of offerings God is looking for.

Diary of a Dangerous Vision by **Andy Hawthorne** – The exciting story of the Message combined with crucial reflections and biblical teaching to equip you to run the race.

The Heart of Worship Files by **Matt Redman** – This book features highlights from the very popular website, heartofworship.com. Compiled by Matt Redman, it will encourage and inspire you to help others reach new depths of worship.

survivor

Facedown
by Matt Redman

"When we face up to the glory of God, we find ourselves facedown in worship."

FACEDOWN worship always begins as a posture of the heart. It's a person so desperate for the increase of Christ that they find themselves decreasing to the ground in acts of reverent submission. A soul so captivated by the Almighty that to bend low in true and total surrender seems the only appropriate response.

Bestselling author of *The Unquenchable Worshipper*, Matt Redman takes us on a journey into wonder, reverence and mystery.

FACEDOWN the album is now available on CD and DVD.

Wasteland?
by Mike Pilavachi

Are you looking for greater depth in your Christian life? Tired of the consumer model of spirituality? Are you ready to do the *right* things, even when things are going *wrong*? Feel like investing in obscurity . . . ? Mountain tops can be invigorating, but there's growth in the valleys. God says, 'Meet me in the desert.'

'Mike Pilavachi draws on his own experience and the Bible to infuse faith, hope and love in us, and to inspire us on our journey.' (J. John, Philo Trust)

survivor